DICK TRACY'S FIENDISH FOES

Selected by
Max Allan Collins
and Dick Locher

ST. MARTIN'S PRESS NEW YORK

To Matt Masterson—Dick Tracy's most fiendish fan.

DICK TRACY'S FIENDISH FOES: A 60TH ANNIVERSARY CELEBRATION. Copyright © 1991 by Tribune Media Services, Inc. All rights reserved. Printed in the United States of America. No part of this book may be used or reproduced in any manner whatsoever without written permission except in the case of brief quotations embodied in critical articles or reviews. For information, address St. Martin's Press, 175 Fifth Avenue, New York, N.Y. 10010.

Production Editor: David Stanford Burr

Design by Glen M. Edelstein

Library of Congress Cataloging-in-Publication Data

Dick Tracy's fiendish foes : a 60th anniversary celebration / selected
  by Max Allan Collins and Dick Locher.
    p.   cm.
  ISBN 0-312-06337-7—ISBN 0-312-06338-5 (pbk.)
  1. Dick Tracy (Comic strip)   I. Collins, Max Allan.   II. Locher,
Dick, 1929–
PN6728.D53D54   1991
741.5'973—dc20   91-21013
                                                                    CIP

First Edition: October 1991

10 9 8 7 6 5 4 3 2 1

CONTENTS

FOREWORD

Five very special golden statuettes adorn the mantle of the Dick Tracy household. Standing next to the two Reuben Awards, which are the equivalent of the Oscar for comic strips, now stand three Hollywood Oscars. They were awarded this year by the Academy of Motion Picture Arts and Sciences to the 1990 movie, *Dick Tracy*.

For sixty years, Tracy has cut a swath, not only in the annals of the comic page but in the sights and sounds of the movie screen. And Detective Tracy is holding up well. His chisel-shaped contours have stopped many bullets. He even has a yellow hat collection at police department headquarters; thirty-two by actual count, and all with bullet holes in them.

He has been run over by his classic villains, thrown from cliffs, skewered, dipped in wax, set ablaze, and frozen. After six decades of abuse, Tracy is a fit specimen, still able to challenge today's modern criminals.

He is holding up well in a different sense. Dick Tracy is not only surviving but thriving after being in the media for sixty years. How many comic characters traveling the comic panels published today can make this claim?

Not only has Dick Tracy received Oscars and Reubens, but the strip also holds special records. Chester Gould was always proud to recount to me the fact that the "Dick Tracy" strip holds the record for a color comic strip appearing on the front page of a newspaper Sunday comic section. Tracy accomplished this feat for forty-five continuous years at the *New York Daily News*.

The following collection of Tracy strips celebrates in a special way sixty years of the best-known gumshoe of all time. It is a fitting tribute to comic lovers and to the comic-*noir* itself. And I was there to witness a good part of it. I worked with Chester Gould in the fifties and sixties. I was Chet's close friend at the *Chicago Tribune* in the seventies when I became an Editorial Cartoonist at the *Trib*. Then, following Chet's retirement, I've been part of the team with Max Collins in the eighties and nineties.

If someone were to ask, "What was the most exciting period for you and Dick Tracy?" it would be difficult for me to answer. It would be similar to the question, "What is your best editorial cartoon?" My answer is, "I haven't done it yet."

So, perhaps the best is yet to come. After sixty years, are you kidding? What else is left for Tracy? He's done it all.

Not by a long shot, I remind myself. There are scenarios and situations waiting for Tracy that you couldn't dream of. Tracy will forever be in "harm's way."

However, one of my favorite escapades for the Master Sleuth took place the first year I worked with Chet. Not only was it a particularly hair-raising scheme for Tracy, but it was one that had our audience eagerly awaiting each day's output. Tracy was in deep trouble.

Mondays were script days at the *Tribune*; we did no artwork. Chet and I just kicked around plots and dastardly deals for Dick. It was the Miss Egghead and Supt. Whitehall series that gave us this delicious opportunity to wipe out the great detective once and for all.

Tracy was unceremoniously dumped into a deserted canyon somewhere in the far reaches of the Caribbean. Supplied with a parachute, Tracy floats down into this high-rimmed goat and lizard infested canyon. Chet turned to me and asked, "Okay, Dick, we have Tracy in this hole, literally! Now how do we get his bacon out?"

I pondered and offered my suggestion. Gould liked it and went with it. You will see my results in the canyon episode.

The real kicker to this adventure came shortly afterward when Chester Gould won the first of his golden statues—a Reuben for this particular episode. He gave me credit and I was delighted.

Chet would be proud of what Max and I are doing today with the great detective. He would love our new characters, such as Putty Puss and Dr. Freezdrei. Who knows? Is there still some space left on that mantle for another tribute to Dick Tracy? Chet would like to think so and so would we! We aren't done yet!

—Dick Locher

INTRODUCTION

A World of Trouble

In 1931, after ten years of occasional success and frequent failure, journeyman cartoonist Chester Gould had nothing to lose.

His most recent strip, "The Girl Friends," running in the Chicago *News* (a pretty-girl feature in the "Boots and Her Buddies" vein) was not setting the world on fire. His many previous strip attempts had seemingly exhausted every comics genre then extant—variations of humor from funny animals to cute kids to domestic sitcom, as well as sports cartoons, editorial panels, and even a "Believe It or Not" knockoff. His major claim to fame was "Fillum Fables," an imitation of Ed Wheelan's "Minute Movies," done reluctantly at the bidding of King Features, which is to say, William Randolph Hearst.

Despite his natural inclination toward humor (Bud Fisher's "Mutt and Jeff" was his favorite comic strip), Gould tried a desperate tact: an adventure strip. Very few of those existed: "Wash Tubbs" and "Tarzan" were just about it. Maybe, if you squinted, you could include the soap opera-ish "Little Orphan Annie." Certainly, there were no detective strips— other than the occasional Sherlock Holmes spoof— and absolutely no strip dealing in the hard-boiled blood-and-thunder thriving in pulp magazines like *Black Mask* and on movie screens, courtesy of the likes of *Little Caesar* and *Public Enemy.*

Every good newspaper cartoonist is to some degree a journalist, and Gould was no exception. He looked around him, in the Chicago of 1931, and saw a violent landscape ruled by Al Capone and his minions. He also noticed a handful of honest federal agents—in particular, one Eliot Ness, whose clean-cut, square-jawed picture was appearing in the local papers just about then—who fit perfectly this Oklahoma-born Conan Doyle fan's notion of an American Sherlock Holmes.

In the samples for his strip—provisionally entitled "Plainclothes Tracy"—Gould pitted his American Holmes against a shameless caricature of Capone. And in so doing, he instituted, right out of the box, two great "Tracy" traditions: the larger-than-life villain and topical crime.

These weren't the only staples of the "Tracy" strip. Over the years, Gould's first love, humor, was present from the start (Scotland Yard man J. Scotland Bumstead, in 1934, for example, and Indian Chief Yellow Pony, in 1935, were but two of many comic-relief secondary characters in the early years);

and humor blossomed big-time in the forties with the likes of Vitamin Flintheart, Gravel Gertie and B.O. Plenty. Also, Gould made a point of including up-to-date police procedure in the strip; Tracy was more likely to use fingerprinting or ballistics or a lie detector to solve his crimes than Holmes-style ratiocination.

There were frequent soap opera-style story lines: tearjerkers in which sympathetic characters died or nearly died; Tracy's long, stormy engagement to Tess Trueheart; Junior's painful street-kid upbringing and his tragic reunion with his father, Hank Steele. As late as 1961, Gould provided a continuity about Junior's loss of his real mother.

And there were glorious cross-country chases. Often, a "Tracy" story was less a detective tale than an extended chase, fraught with peril for both the pursued and the pursuer. The influence of such real-life on-the-run outlaws as Pretty Boy Floyd (the model for Flattop) and John Dillinger upon these extended chases is undeniable.

Still, the single most famous aspect of the "Tracy" strip is Gould's lineup of vivid villains. No one, including Tracy's creator, ever denied that the bad guys were more interesting than the hero. Many a Gould continuity spends more time with the evil-doer than the two-fisted but straight-laced Tracy. When Flattop "died," telegrams of condolence and truckloads of flowers arrived at Gould's home and office by way of mourning.

And by way of scolding Tracy's imaginative creator. "How," these fans were saying, "could you? How could you rob us of so wonderful a fiend?"

But it was Gould's credo that "crime does not pay"; that the crooks "never win"—hence, most of his villains appear but once in the strip . . . often dying grisly, ironic deaths that preclude their return. Gould's attitude was that there were "plenty more where they came from," meaning of course, his fertile imagination. What would have become of Batman, had the Joker, Penguin, and Catwoman appeared but once?

Occasionally Gould made an exception. One of his strongest early villains appeared a record three times: Stooge Viller. Mumbles made two appearances, as did the Mole, belatedly (as you will see).

But usually dead was dead, in "Dick Tracy." Chester Gould loved to kid, but he did not kid around.

2

And as the fortunate successor to Gould as scriptwriter of "Dick Tracy," I have been unfortunate in one major way: That wonderful legacy of villains is largely unavailable to me. Because Dick Tracy—and Chester Gould—killed the bad guys dead, dead, dead.

Perhaps Gould knew he'd made at least one mistake, in bumping off the popular Flattop, and he undid this by presenting Flattop's equally vile son, in a story (included here) that may well outshine the original.

This has paved the way for me to create Angeltop, Flattop's "little girl," and several other second-generation villains, including most recently Restless Mahoney, niece of Breathless (not really a crook) and Hi-Top, the mulatto street-gang grandson of Flattop.

And in two key instances, I have managed to *un*-kill two of Gould's greatest villains . . . and the results of these experiments are included here as well.

To celebrate the sixtieth anniversary of the strip's birth, it seemed fitting to assemble an album of Tracy's most famous, fiendish foes; but previous volumes by various publishers—as well as a well-produced recent series of comic books by Gladstone—have already gathered the Gould continuities featuring Tracy's most famous foes.

Centering on the nostalgic thirties and forties, however, these volumes neglect Gould's strong work of the fifties. The year 1956 is a particularly good one and features the long, wild Flattop, Jr., story . . . presented here in its entirety.

Gould created many a memorable villainess, and one of the best, Miss Egghead, is represented in this book in a memorable sequence from around the time the strip won the National Cartoonist Society Reuben Award.

Another relative of a foe turned up in 1971—Molene, granddaughter of the Mole, who also resurfaces in the same chaotically imaginative continuity. This rare example of a classic Gould villain making a second appearance has never been reprinted before.

Two more classic Gould villains—Mumbles and Pruneface—return in two of my own continuities, drawn respectively by Gould assistants Rick Fletcher and Dick Locher. And the most popular of the post-Gould villains, Putty Puss, closes out the celebration, fittingly enough in a wax museum populated by Chester Gould's fabulous grotesques.

In assembling this collection, Dick Locher and I have done our best to honor the great detective's sixtieth birthday by inviting as many of his worst enemies to the party as possible. And we have included only stories that have never before been reprinted in book form.

We have also included an interview with Chester Gould, conducted by top "Tracy" fan Matt Masterson and myself in 1980, the only time Chet and I sat down to chat about "Tracy," together, on the record. And I have provided brief introductory notes for each story.

We would like to thank editor Gordon Van Gelder for diligent work in pulling together the disparate elements of this collection; Elyce Small Goldstein of TMS, for similar valiant service; Rick Marschall, editor of *NEMO*, where the Chester Gould interview first appeared; Matt Masterson, who provided many of the strips reprinted in this volume; and Chester Gould's daughter, Mrs. Jean O'Connell, who provided photostats from her father's private files and lent this project her loving support.

Our only regret is that Chester Gould is not here to help blow out the candles on this big, rich cake; if he were, he would no doubt figure out a way for the fire to spread and cause his American Holmes a world of trouble . . .

. . . leaving the villain of the piece burned to a charred crisp—*they can't win!*

—Max Allan Collins

A CONVERSATION WITH CHESTER GOULD

The Chester Gould interview was conducted by Max Collins and Matt Masterson on September 19, 1980. It was transcribed by Heidi MacDonald, and was edited by Collins and Rick Marschall.

COLLINS: Dick is heading into his sixth decade. The thirties, forties, fifties, sixties, seventies, and now the eighties. You've handled five decades, and I'm working on the sixth decade, and hopefully the seventh, eighth, and ninth, and so on. Why do you think that "Dick Tracy" as a comic strip and Dick Tracy as a character have been able to maintain popularity and span so many, many decades and so many readers?

Tracy in action.

GOULD: Well, I think the main reason is the hinge of it was its very unusual intriguing entertainment quality. Not only the characters, but the story, I think, held the newspaper reader's interest. He's the guy that buys the paper, and when he quits, we're out of business.

COLLINS: That's right.

MASTERSON: Chet has some interesting thoughts on the comic strip and its shrinking size as opposed to television, and how the TV industry has really outwitted the newspaper industry.

GOULD: I do think that newspaper editors in many cases have throttled the bait that television planted years ago. Television has, if anything, downgraded comics, saying that comics are not intellectual and they have no so-called educational qualities. And that's all pure bunk to discourage papers from using comics. And what has happened is that television,

which started out with a two-and-a half-inch screen, quickly enlarged that screen to the present, large television screen, making a great visual appeal to the viewer. And newspapers, which formerly had their comics in six columns, cut them down to a scant three columns. A lot of old people can't even read the comics; the hurry-up businessman, riding a commuter train to work, doesn't want to take time to decipher balloons which are so very small, almost imperceptible, and very difficult to read on trains. In other words, the papers have caused their own problems by reducing what I call the original newspaper television. The comic strip was television in the early days of newspapers and they have taken that thing that in many cases made their circulation, given it a boot in the fanny, and reduced it to such a small size it can't be read. I don't think that's good salesmanship and I don't think it's a good circulation technique. But I don't happen to be running too many newspapers at the moment.

COLLINS: Well, why do you think newspaper editors have such a lack of respect for comic strips?

GOULD: I think if somebody preaches a negative situation to you or me long enough we begin to believe it. I believe that they have been brainwashed to their own disadvantage.

COLLINS: By whom?

GOULD: Today news is furnished to you by TV as much as eighteen hours before you might see the same story in your paper. I think the role of the newspaper dispensing news is pretty hard put, so I think the newspaper has to furnish an entertainment product—such as comics strips. If I were—and I'm not so I can say this—if I were presently owner or publisher or editor of a paper, I would make it a practice immediately to print two of my comics at the bottom of the front page every day—

COLLINS: Hmm . . .

GOULD: —just as a matter of headlines at the top. Two comics at the bottom of the front page. I think that would do an awful lot to bring back the great prestige that newspapers used to have. They used to fight to get certain strips, they would outbid each other.

COLLINS: When you were a boy in Pawnee, Oklahoma, what comic strips first caught your fancy?

GOULD: Well, I bought a St. Louis paper as a boy. I

would go to the newsstands, sometime on Saturday afternoons the St. Louis paper would come in, and Sunday morning—the *Chicago Tribune.* This was before the "Gumps," before "Harold Teen" and all that. They had "Mama's Angel Child" and they had a couple of comics. I can't recall their names at the moment. But I would take those home along with the St. Louis paper that I'd gotten the previous afternoon and those became sacred sheets of paper to me. I would keep them until next week, until I got the one next week, and read them over and over.

COLLINS: Which strips? I think I've heard you mention "Mutt and Jeff" as being one of your favorites.

GOULD: "Mutt and Jeff" was in the *Daily Oklahoman* as a daily strip, but we had one running at that time in St. Louis called "Slim Jim."

COLLINS: Oh yes.

GOULD: And "Mama's Angel Child." That was drawn by, I believe, a girl, and it was a cute little thing.

COLLINS: How about people like George McManus and "Bringing Up Father" and "The Katzenjammer Kids"? Were these favorites of yours?

GOULD: "The Katzenjammer Kids" were certainly one of my favorites. But I don't think I got them in either the St. Louis paper or the *Chicago Tribune.* But I don't know . . . I read them, believe me, I got a hold of a paper that had them because I remember . . .

COLLINS: Last night we were talking about "Hairbreadth Harry" as being a strip that you liked.

GOULD: Yeah, "Hairbreadth Harry." I don't know where I saw that, but I saw it years ago.

COLLINS: So that kind of sparked your interest in comics, as a young kid?

GOULD: Oh yes. I decided when I was seven years old I wanted to do cartoons and I never lost that determination.

COLLINS: Your father was in the printing business?

GOULD: Yes, he was. He worked in a weekly newspaper and they took a service of cartoons, editorial cartoons, not the comic strips—and I used to copy those, take them and study them and. . .

COLLINS: Didn't your father display the first showing of Chester Gould artwork?

GOULD: Yes, at the age of seven. The Democrats in Pawnee County were having a county convention they called it, and my dad, in an effort to discourage me I guess—at seven years old, you can't argue with your father!—so Dad said, "If you want to draw why don't you go in the courthouse this afternoon after school and sketch some of the politicians?" Well, it sounded pretty good to me, so I did all my work on the scrap paper from the cutting machine, and I got the best pieces of it, the most recent cuttings, put them under my arm and went and made some sketches—and I could imagine how bad they must have been—but Dad would say, "Who's this?" Well, I had a man in the corner, I was putting different names. . .

MRS. GOULD: I'm going to town, Honey, then I'll be back. Do you want anything?

GOULD: Not a thing, darling, except you. [*laughter*]

COLLINS: We were back in the window at Pawnee print shop.

GOULD: Yeah, the surveyor of Pawnee County, I remember, I can't think of his name, but a big fat guy. He pointed out the different names: "That's so-and-so, that's so-and-so." And I made these sketches and took them to my dad. And he immediately went over and put them against the window. I don't think there was Scotch Tape, but he found some way to glue them to the window in lines. And so what happened was that Pawnee was designed around the square, but the east side of the square had no business at all, just a livery stable. To get to the Post Office, all businessmen had to walk on past the *Courier Dispatch*, Dad's paper, and I remember staying after school the next day and people were still gawking at these pictures. I saw them and they'd look at them and say something and point and then they'd kind of give over a guffaw and I thought, "This is for me, this is my business", and that really clinched my thinking. I wanted to be a cartoonist.

COLLINS: What other art experience did you have as a child and as a young man? Did you do sign painting. . .

GOULD: Oh yeah. I guess many cartoonists do that. It's pretty lucrative in a small town if you get . . . if you can paint signs reasonably well. And I did window jobs, doors on offices, and I did outdoor stuff on barns.

COLLINS: Any memorable experiences in that line of work?

GOULD: Oh, yeah. I had one. There was a guy that ran the hardware store and he also sold paint. Out in the country of Pawnee was a doctor's farm, Doc Waters, and old Doc Waters had a barn that you could see about a mile away, you could see the side of the barn. You couldn't read it that far away but as you came down the road it got bigger and bigger and there it was. So this hardware store man, his name was Brewington, he said, "I'd like to have a sign painted on that side of Doc Waters's barn, can you do it?", and I said "Sure I can do it!" And he said, "Well, I'll give you a great twenty-five dollars, and I'll furnish the paint." So that was big dough; I was barely sixteen then. Well, I went out there and put the sign on—a typical thing, Brewington for Fine Furniture, Quality and Price, and all that sort of stuff, a typical small-town ad. Brewington always had a format in his signs, down in the corner he always had a picture of what was supposed to be Brewington's head. He'd paint the head in there and it said "Our Founder." Brewington was kind of a heady fellow, too, goodlooking and very influential in town. So I painted it and put "Our Founder" and I got the paint all down and I invited him to see it. He paid me my twenty-five dollars and the next day I heard from him as I went to school—I had to pass his place—and he said to me "Listen, you painted that sign, and that's all right. But have you been there lately?" Well, the weather had gotten a little hot and it so happened I had painted over Dutch doors, at each end of the barn. And where I had "Our Founder," the farmer—it was getting warm—he had the upper part of the dutch door open, and it said Our Founder and you could see the ass and the tail of a big Prussian horse. [*general laughter*] It happened! Everybody had to laugh at Brewington.

COLLINS: Chet, you had another experience with, I believe, it was the mayor of the town. You painted his—

GOULD: Oh yeah, I got seventy-five cents on a big contract deal to put J. V. ORTON, MAYOR, right at the top of the stairs on his door. So after I got the sign on, I asked him to come out take a look at it, and he said well, the lettering was all right. It was just black lettering. He said, "But I don't think it's worth seventy-five cents." And I said, "Well, that's what we agreed on." He said, "Tell ya what, I'll give ya fifty cents for it." I had a razor blade in my pocket in a little box. I took out this single-edged blade. I didn't say anything, I just went over there and just scraped off the whole sign, like that, and went downstairs.

COLLINS: [*laughs*] Don't fool around with Gould.

GOULD: No, I was always proud of that. And I didn't know what he did, I don't know, probably wished to hell he'd kept his finger out of it.

COLLINS: Not all the jobs you had were artistic, though. Didn't you work as a soda jerk or at a soda fountain?

GOULD: Oh yeah, I did duty as a soda jerk at both drug stores at different times of course. And it was very pleasant. It was big-time business in the summer; one of the most lucrative things that the drug store had then was the soda fountain in the summer. Jay's Drug Store had about six of these big ceiling fans, two over the soda fountain, which was, oh, about twenty-five or thirty feet long; it was a big soda fountain. And it was so pleasant there. I enjoyed it very much. And the big thing about it—I got fifteen dollars a week. You get to work about 7:00 in the morning, and you quit about 7:00 in the evening. But it was good experience.

COLLINS: Well, the story I'm fishing for is the one about the Indians who came in.

GOULD: Oh yes; oh, well, the Indians were very fond of red, and of course, in terms of the soda, an ice-cream soda, the only reds were the cherries and the strawberries, so when I'd see a couple of Indians coming, I'd know what to expect. "Give me red."

MASTERSON: Chet, what was the first piece you had printed in a magazine?

GOULD: *The American Boy.* Do you remember the magazine *The American Boy*? They had a contest during World War I for any boy, all boys under sixteen. There was a prize, I think of ten dollars, and they would print the winning cartoon. Well, I got into it and I got first prize, and this magazine printed it. Somewhere in my old trunk, it's probably still there, but I wouldn't dig it out. What I did, I had a company of soldiers, marching down this dirt road, and there was a boy in a cornfield. It was a hot, sunny day, and he was hoeing it . . . they used to hoe corn instead of cultivate it with a team because they could get all the little weeds without harming the corn. The corn got so big they couldn't very well drive a team down the row, they'd knock it down. So they had a horrible, horrible job of hoeing the corn. Hotter than hell, no air . . . So anyway, this kid was hoeing this, and one soldier was looking at him, they were looking right at each other and the title

of it is "What A Stint He's Got." One guy going to war and the other hoeing corn. Each coveting the other's job.

COLLINS: When did you leave home to go out to work on your own?

GOULD: I left Pawnee, Oklahoma, in 1921.

COLLINS: And you were then twenty-one?

GOULD: I would be twenty-one in November. I arrived in Chicago September 1. I left Pawnee the last day of August. And I've got a good little story about that that's based on realism. That was about the time that gangsters began, started to flourish in Chicago, you know. So when I arrived in town, I had fifty bucks, and that was a lot of money, believe me, in those days that would be about equal to $350 today. I knew that would carry me over until I had money coming in. Well, I'd been there about a week when I got a letter from my mother and she said, "I've been reading in the *Daily Oklahoman* about these gangsters that are in Chicago. They're shooting people down on the street, and robbing them, and you're up there with fifty dollars in your pocket! Come home at once." [*general laughter*]

COLLINS: But you didn't go home?

GOULD: I didn't go home. I wrote my mother a letter and said, "Look, from what I understand, decent people don't have anything to worry about, these guys are shooting each other down," and I said, "You can be sure that I'm safe and sound." I had to pacify her.

MASTERSON: What was your first job, then?

GOULD: Strange to say, within a couple of days I landed a job on the old *Chicago Journal.* The reason I got it, I just happened to be there at the right time. One of the guys in the art department had to go to the hospital for an appendectomy. And the second guy in command who was then in charge, he looked at my art that I'd brought from Oklahoma, editorial cartoons from the *Tulsa Democrat* and sports cartoons from the *Daily Oklahoman*, and he said, "Well these aren't exactly big-city stuff, but until our man gets back from the hospital, be about a month that's all, I could put you on at thirty dollars a week." Well, I just about busted a gut standing there. Thirty dollars a week, man! So I went in there and I got thirty dollars a week for the month of September, and came October 1, he was back and I picked up my coat and hat and I was out on the street again. But that was my first job. So . . .

COLLINS: That gave you some professional credentials of a sort.

GOULD: Oh, it did. And I had listed every newspaper, starting first at the *Tribune.* I went to the *Journal* and the *Post,* the *Herald Examiner* and the *Evening American.* I hit the art departments of all those newspapers. But I couldn't get in anywhere after the *Journal* and that month-long deal; there was nothing. So I put most of my money in the bank. I knew I had a little backlog in the savings department. So I kind of treaded water for a day or two, not very long. And I finally picked up the want ads. And out on Vaughn Avenue, there was an A&P store looking for a stock boy. That's the guy who carries all the cans around and puts them on the shelf and all that. And I said, "Well then, I'll do that," any-

thing. And I went out there and applied for that job as stock boy. And they said "We just hired him. See that guy over there? We just hired him. We don't need a stock boy." So I got on the street car, went back to where I had a room on South Street, and said "What do I do now?" Well, a fellow that I met in a cigar store two or three times gave me a tip. I told him I was looking for art jobs. He said, "I happen to know a place on South Dearborn where they lost one of their men. Why don't you go down there?" Zuckerman was the man's name who owned the place. He ran a little ad service where they would make up plates like "Year End Sale" and "Going Out of Business," that sort of stuff. Stock stuff that little papers could put in whenever a store wanted them to. I went down there. I wasn't a commercial artist in the sense of being able to draw men's fashions but they made me an office boy, and I pasted stuff down and erased drawings and carried things over to the engraving house and did all the things that an office boy would do in the big city. And I was there almost a year. In the meantime, I had been going back to all of these art departments, no matter how they treated me—they couldn't insult me, they couldn't depress me because I had confidence and I knew I was going to make it.

COLLINS: How often did you make the rounds?

GOULD: Well, I tried to see each one at least once a week, and that would be quite often on Saturday mornings. Because they all had Saturday editions in the art department there was no such thing as a five-day week. Your week wasn't complete until one o'clock Saturday. Then everything, the offices, all closed and everybody went home. So I was able to contact two or three of these outfits on Saturday morning. A guy by the name of Haggerty—that was the guy in the cigar store who told me about Zuckerman's place—was assistant art director of the Copy and Art Service of the *Chicago Tribune*. That was the last damn place I wanted to go. I wanted to go to the *Tribune* as a comic strip artist, with an exclusive office with my name on the door. But he said that he could put me on here until I got established; he was very sympathetic—he said, "We don't handle many cartoons, we have little one-columns, sometimes on the front page or a special story, just a little one-column thing." He said, "The editorial department would send up what they want and we do that. I may get one or two of those for you, but in the meantime you will erase drawings, and you're pretty good at lettering, you may get a chance to do some lettering." And I believe he said it would be fifty dollars a week.

COLLINS: A fortune.

GOULD: That was a fortune. I began to sense that I was breaking into the Chicago scene a little bit, so I kept making the rounds of the newspapers.

COLLINS: With strips?

GOULD: Oh yeah, in the meantime at night I would work on a strip or two, or sport cartoons, editorials, anything.

MASTERSON: Ripley's *Believe It or Not* type of thing?

GOULD: Yes, I did have one on that order. But my campaign at the moment was one of the Hearst papers. It was the *Evening American*, and a little guy by the name of Curley—just like old Boston's mayor, the same name—was in charge at the *American*, and he was Hearst's top man in the editing line. He was later taken away from Chicago and put in charge of five eastern Hearst papers: Boston, New York, Philadelphia, Pittsburgh, whatever. And so I met him and he was very nice. He would talk and listen, and he said, "Let me see what you've got, but I can't promise you anything at all, it has to come from New York. If I think you've got anything, I'll tell you to send it to New York, to King Features." Well, I loaded him with stuff pretty fast and got nowhere. At that time, Hearst had a cartoonist named Kettner, I believe, who had a funny line drawing, but Hearst thought he was great. He just drew empty lines, no shadowing or anything. *[EDITOR'S NOTE: Gould is here referring to T. E. Powers, of whom Maurice Ketten was one of several imitators.]* Strictly editorial sort of stuff. He had one little group of people he called Joys, and another he called Glooms. And if he was drawing an editorial that had to do with the dark side of something he had a bunch of these Glooms marching around in the story. He was a way-out cartoonist. I never did like his stuff, but Hearst thought he was great and so did Curley. And it ran four columns about that deep on the back page of the *American*. And it was an insult to me because I couldn't stand the guy's stuff and he was getting all this space. So . . . I was still working on the *Tribune* in commercial art. And one day I drew an editorial cartoon just exactly the proportions of this [*Powers*] stuff. And I went into the *American*'s own engraving room and said I'd like to get a cut made of this, and I got a hold of some newsprint from another fellow there, just regular news stuff. I had them pull a proof of this cartoon, and I got it out and pasted it in right over [*Power's*] cartoon, exactly. At first glance it looked like Gould was in the *American*. I knew that the scrub women came into Curley's office about 5:30 and I saw to it that I was up there one day, and I walked in and took this cartoon. The scrub woman thought that I worked in the editorial room, in shirt sleeves and everything. And I put it on [*Curley's*] desk; he had a very husky but pleasant secretary called Miss Dougherty and I put it down and got the heck out of there. Well, about ten o'clock in the morning the next day, over at the *Tribune*, the phone rang and it was for me. Haggerty called me and said, "It's for you." So I thought my wife is calling me, but it was Miss Dougherty, and she said, "Can you get over here and see Mr. Curley sometime today?" Well, if she'd asked if I could jump out the tenth floor of that building I'd have said, "Yes, I certainly can!" So I said "Yes, I'll be over there, probably about ten minutes after eleven." I went out at 11:00, and I went over there, and he had this thing in front of him and he said, "Did you draw this?" and I said that I did, and he said, "Well, you damn near fooled me. I wanted to know who would sanction this. I think the best way to get rid of you is to hire you." [*general laughter*] So he put me on and put me up another ten dollars a week, that made sixty bucks, that was essentially my way of breaking into Chicago. I was at the

American six years.

COLLINS: Now what year was that?

GOULD: 1923.

COLLINS: What work did you do there?

GOULD: What work didn't I do, is a good question. One day I had, I believe, eleven cartoons in one issue of the *American.* I did little one column illustrations, I did sports cartoons, I did an editorial cartoon. I kept a lot of this stuff handy, see, so it wouldn't get out of date on a general subject. And when they wanted a cartoon, I gave it to them.

COLLINS: Is that the paper that you did the strip for that was a news strip?

GOULD: Well, I did two cartoons. Curley said he wanted me to draw a strip about radio. Radio was very fresh and new, and getting bigger, much like the impact of television. The most common set of the day was what they call a crystal set; it had no tubes or no internal maintenance at all, but there was a little cat's whisker that you fooled around with and it touched this stone, this little hunk of stone, with a handle back here, and you hit a certain spot and you got the reception. No tubes, no batteries, no nothing. That was very common and successful, so I named this strip "The Radio Cats" after the cat's whisker. They were Siamese cats. That was my radio strip. The other one he wanted me to do was a takeoff on Ed Wheelan's "Minute Movies," and I came up with one called "Fillum Fables." So I had two strips running in the *American* every day, besides the stuff that they would bring in to me.

COLLINS: Now, did those strips run in any other papers?

GOULD: They finally picked up "Fillum Fables" for the *Journal* in New York, but it never got . . . King never took it, and it never got wide syndication. It was a rather lousy imitation of Ed Wheelan, is what it was. I didn't want to do that—I wanted to do my own stuff, my original stuff.

COLLINS: Now "Fillum Fables" was a continuity; "Radio Cats"—was that a humor strip?

GOULD: That was a humor strictly. "Fillum Fables" was a burlesque.

COLLINS: When did you do the strips that were news strips where you would talk about things happening in the city in comic-strip format? They weren't editorials.

GOULD: "Why It's a Windy City"?

COLLINS: Yes, "Why It's a Windy City."

GOULD: I went in to Curley one day, and said that I'd got an idea for him, kind of Walter Winchell in cartoon, called "Why It's a Windy City"; I would interview big shots and businessmen. He said, "Sounds all right, give me a couple." So I remember the first one I did was of the manager of the Congress hotel, and he was a sassy son of a bitch, but I told him I was starting a new column in cartoons, that Mr. Curley, the managing editor, said he would like it to consist of a funny anecdote or any comment that someone like you would like to make each day. If someone like you makes a comment, I'll have it made. So I finally got him on my side, and I would get about three of those a day, by doing a lot of talking. It took a lot of walking around the Loop. And it was highly successful. It got a hell of a lot of comment.

Various sample humor strips of Chester Gould's (previously unpublished).

John Barrymore's thespian counterpart, Vitamin Flintheart.

COLLINS: Did you interview any well-known celebrities for that column?

GOULD: Well, when I was over in town I would. I had comments from all the show people that were in town.

COLLINS: Any big names?

GOULD: I had Eddie Cantor and Al Jolson, Ed Wynn, a couple of the dramatic actors. I can't recall it all.

COLLINS: Did Vitamin Flintheart's counterpart, Lionel Barrymore, get in the Windy city?

GOULD: [*laughs*] I don't think I ever did interview a Barrymore, although they were in the shows constantly in those days. But I just never got around to them.

COLLINS: Was that before or after or at the same time as "Radio Cats" and "Fillum Fables"?

GOULD: "Radio Cats" and "Fillum Fables" were going on all the time.

COLLINS: Well, when did you sleep?

GOULD: I didn't sleep. The Lord gave me one hell of a good body, let me tell you. I'd be sitting there when the Art Department was going home at the *American*, and the Art Department was right in the editorial room, what they called the newsroom. There were four fellows, and their day was over when the last edition of the *American* was out. It was an afternoon paper, and that last edition came out just about the time when the commuters were going home, so they would get this hot off the press, and after that the boys got up and put on their coats, folded their *Americans* under their arms and said "Goodnight." I'd say "Goodnight." And they'd come down next morning, and most of the time I'd be sitting there just finishing up something. And one would say, "Hey guys, come here! He's still here." And the other'd say, "He's nuts! What do you do? When do you sleep?" And I'd just keep on working. And they got my goat there once or twice, but then I laughed it off, and said *they* have to go home and do things but I don't. I had no family, nobody I was responsible to. No reason to be home at five o'clock. I can just sit here and work, and I said, "I'll do the work of two men, with the body I've got, I'll do the work of two men, and I will get to my goal in half the time that these monkeys will even if they work hard. In other words, I'm on a fast train, doing two lifetimes while they flounder through one."

COLLINS: The theory being that if you do away with sleep you pick up an extra day's work.

GOULD: An extra life, year. I would work right through the night at least two nights a week.

COLLINS: You finally left Hearst and "Fillum Fables" because you were tired of doing what you considered to be an imitation of Wheelan, is that correct?

GOULD: Well, that was part of it. The rest of it was that I had submitted several original ideas to them, and they wanted to keep me on "Fillum Fables" and I wanted to get away from that, because it was not my original idea.

COLLINS: And around this time you were, in a roundabout way, approached about possibly doing "Little Annie Rooney." You were never directly approached, but that was one of the things that was bandied about.

GOULD: I think it was suddenly passed around to different art departments at Hearst, but that was not for me.

COLLINS: The thing you did in between "Fillum Fables" and "Tracy" was this strip for the *Daily News* in Chicago, called "The Girl Friends." How did you come to do that strip?

GOULD: Well, while I was drawing rugs and canned corn and stuff for the regular daily ads I was told to come into the office of the editor of the *News*. I didn't know if I was going to get fired or what. He said, "I understand you have some experience with the *American*." I said yes. "Well, we need a girl strip in the *Daily News*," and he asked if I could draw a girl strip and I said, "I sure can!" So he said "Well, let me see a couple and we might start using them right here in the *News*." That was the way I got into "The Girl Friends."

COLLINS: And then very shortly after that "Tracy" began. When you prepared the samples for "Dick Tracy" you had at that time prepared dozens, perhaps a hundred, samples of strips that had not sold. When you did "Tracy" for the first time, then "Plainclothes Tracy," did you have a certain hunch about it or a tingle about it?

GOULD: Oh yeah, I felt that it would either go to the top or fall on its face. I was afraid that Patterson might be offended by it because it was so rough, and say, "I don't like that," and as it turned out, Patterson was wild about "Dick Tracy" right from the beginning. That was the kind of stuff that he wanted in his paper.

COLLINS: Well, you had a sequence in that very first five-strip sample in which you actually had the Al

"The Girl Friends," 1931. Note the resemblances of characters in the top strip to Tess Trueheart and Dick Tracy.

Capone character, Big Boy, using a blow torch on someone's feet, which was pretty rough stuff for the day. Nothing like that had ever appeared in a comic strip before. But Patterson ate that up, apparently.

GOULD: He felt it would sell papers.

COLLINS: And that was the name of the game.

GOULD: That was the name of the game, and it still is today. We have become so compromising about everything that's in newspapers that they all look alike today. Any newspaper you can buy in any part of the country, they've got the same news. They have the same type of thinking, the same columns of sob sisters, of political hacks, or whatever. The

Broadway Bates threatens to give Tracy "the works."

[*New York*] *News* was individual, to say the least.

COLLINS: I don't know if anybody has ever asked you this. But you had been at it for a good ten years and while you had had a considerable success in Chicago on a local level, you had been struggling to break through with that national comic strip for ten years. Dozens and dozens of samples. At this point in your life, in 1931, were you at a low ebb or were you prepared to do another ten years? Had it begun to get to you?

GOULD: I was prepared mentally to go to my grave if necessary, but I was determined to get something for my efforts, and I said I can't miss—the practice and the effort that I'm putting in, the repetitive labor I'm putting into this stuff, it's bound to bring some kind of reward.

COLLINS: Well, you spent ten years trying, doing things like "Radio Cats," "Fillum Fables," "The Girl Friends." Would you agree with me that those were probably the ten most important years in your career, those preparatory years?

GOULD: Oh, I think they were. I think they're the most important in any young man's life, the immediate ten or fifteen years before he lands what he wants. Now remember, I had a lot of experience, what we called big-time experience in Oklahoma. I was called down to Tulsa, the Tulsa *Democrat,* when I was nineteen, to do editorial cartoons for one month to fight a bond issue to build a new water reservoir. Well, the opposition paper was for the bond issue. The paper that hired me was against the bond issue. My side lost, and my career as an editorial cartoonist ended at the end of that campaign, but in the meantime I had made contacts with the *Daily Oklahoman* through my association at State College, and I made arrangements with the sporting editor that I would send in a cartoon every other week—a resume of the week's sports in Oklahoma.

COLLINS: When you went to Chicago, to backtrack a little bit, in 1921, did you have a four-year college degree at that time?

GOULD: No. I had two years. I immediately enrolled in night school. The very next day after I landed my first job, [*I*] was to go find out where to get into night school.

COLLINS: Are you telling me that those first years when you were turning out all that material, you were going to college too?

GOULD: That's right. Well, I didn't sleep. Yeah, I went to school and finished up my course in commerce and marketing school.

COLLINS: Do you think that explains why even though you're an artist, you've had the outlook and attitude of a businessman all these years?

GOULD: I think it's had a great deal to do with it.

COLLINS: And with your success?

GOULD: Well, I abhorred the artist that lived in the garret and gave himself up as a sacrifice on the fires of human endeavor because he was an artist. I said, "They're not for me, those jerks."

COLLINS: You did not dress like a bohemian.

GOULD: No, I tried my best to look like a banker, and in those days bankers looked like bankers.

COLLINS: Chet, after all of your efforts to get on the *Tribune,* "Dick Tracy" did not begin

Chester and Edna Gould, circa 1935. Photographer unknown.

in the *Tribune,* did it?

GOULD: That's right, it didn't. Well, I want to tell you a little bit. Patterson spent most of his time in New York at the *News* in those days. I thought if I put all my samples in a grip and could go down and sit with him personally and let him see what I can do, it might help. So I put everything that I thought was big-league—not the junk from childhood but the stuff I thought had possibilities—in a black bag and went down, and he very graciously said to come in, and I showed him what I had, and then he looked through all of it. He didn't slight anything. He said "Well, you've done a lot of work here," and he said, "We cannot use any of what you have, but whenever you get anything that you think could be worthwhile, send it to me." And I came back, and I was greatly heartened that he had looked at my stuff, and he did say to me the last thing he said, "Right now, Mr. Gould, I'm looking for a cartoonist, an editorial cartoonist. You have some editorials here, but they're from Oklahoma and I can't tell too much about them." They were clippings. So what I did—I didn't tell him—but I said I'll see if I can get something and send it to you, so I went right downstairs and subscribed for six months to the *Sunday* and *Daily News,* and I think that was around fifty bucks, to be sent to me in Illinois.

The *News* began to come, and I would read the editorial page, every damn line in the editorial, not the "Voice of the People" and all that, but the direct editorial, I read it every day. In fact I cut them out and refreshed myself every so often. At the end of two weeks I hit on a plan. I was then going to Chicago six days a week. We were then living in Woodstock, this was when everyone worked until one o'clock, all the conventional people did. And I would do an editorial cartoon at night. I had envelopes that I had gotten at wherever I worked last time, that would just fit in a certain size I was drawing these cartoons. I would put a piece of corrugated wood in there, address it to J. M. Patterson, New York *Daily News,* 220 East Forty-second Street, and every day for thirty days, including Sunday, I walked to the mail car of the Twentieth Century and handed it to the guy, all stamped and ready to go, first-class, and after a week or so they thought I was a big shot who was sending some goddamn important stuff to

New York, and then, you know, it was "Hello" and "Hi" and "How Are You Doing Today," and I sent that for thirty days.

I call that the greatest masterpiece of salesmanship I ever did. So every morning, Patterson came down, including Monday morning, and there was a cartoon by Gould. I didn't hear anything from him. And finally I got a package from Miss Higgins who was his secretary; it said that the Captain likes these very much but he doesn't seem to believe your style is what he's looking for. They made her hire C. D. Batchelor, that kind of breezy, sketchy—he was powerful, too, his stuff was great, and he wasn't yet hired. Well, about the next day after I got that, I got a letter from Patterson. It said, "I thank you so much for letting me see the cartoons which came in every day. They are not quite what I'm looking for but please see that I get any other material that you might think I would be interested in . . . I told Edna. "I got a job!" [laughs]

COLLINS: You knew you were on the trail.

GOULD: "I'm hired!" I felt I was hired. I didn't think there was any question about it. I was hired, just by those words.

COLLINS: This was shortly before "Dick Tracy."

GOULD: Yeah, he hadn't seen "Dick Tracy" yet. So this was in, I think, the spring of thirty-one. I'm a little vague. It could have been—cold weather I think, the month I did that it was cold weather. But anyway I got the idea for "Plainclothes Tracy."

COLLINS: I know this is a silly, clichéd question, but do you know how you got that idea? What springboarded it for you?

GOULD: Nothing sparked it. I was just a great follower of Sherlock Holmes on the radio for G. Washington Coffee. And [it was] a very good radio program, very thrilling, exciting. In fact I would say that in all America, it was the most highly thought-of dramatic show on the air. I said "Hell, I'm going to do a detective. I never sold the guy anything, he can't do any more than throw it out the window, so . . ."

COLLINS: What gave you the notion to make it a modern detective as opposed to the traditional Sherlock Holmes—

GOULD: I'm reading the *Daily News*, and it was the biggest circulated paper, over two million, and three million and a half Sunday, and I said anything that can draw *that* many subscribers or people or buyers, that's what I've got to have.

COLLINS: Let me simplify this a little bit. Would it be fair to say that the thing that really occurred to you was this: "What if Sherlock Holmes were alive today and fighting Al Capone." Is that kind of the idea?

GOULD: Well, I used those very words. I said if Holmes were alive today as a young man, he wouldn't wear the two-peaked cap, and he'd have a snap-brim fedora and [he'd] probably be wearing a camel's hair coat and that was the way I built Tracy.

COLLINS: So instead of Professor Moriarty, he took on the Chicago mob.

GOULD: Right. And this combined with the fact that Chicago was in the throes of death and gangsters. I said, "I'm going to make a detective. They've got fixed juries, they've got fixed judges, they've got all kinds of crooked business going on, they can't get a conviction, hoodlums come in the court after being involved in a murder and the lawyers get them out. They bring 'em in around 8:30 in the morning, and the lawyers have them walking the streets at 11:30."

COLLINS: Chet, it's well known that you were drawing a Persian rug, or an Oriental rug, when you got the telegram from Captain Patterson telling you that "Plainclothes Tracy" had possibilities. Can you tell us a little bit about that first meeting with Captain Patterson and how that went? You followed up on that telegram . . .

GOULD: All my experiences with Patterson had been slowly getting better and I sent him these editorials and I sent one week of "Plainclothes Tracy" and it was just as if I had dropped off a cliff. Nothing, absolutely nothing. Well, August eighteenth, did I tell you about Edna reading the telegram over the phone? She said, "I have a telegram here from Captain Patterson," and I was doing an Oriental rug. I was going over a silver-print of a rug for Ocean Silver Company. They're still in business, I guess; they're a big outfit. I said, "Read the telegram, I want to get my damn rug done. It's monotonous." She said, "BELIEVE PLAINCLOTHES TRACY HAS POSSIBILITIES. SEE ME IN CHICAGO THE TWENTIETH. CALL MY SECRETARY FOR TIME". . . . or something like that. I said, "Well, for Chrissake, it took him long enough."

COLLINS: But you were pretty happy . . .

GOULD: I was fed up. I was really fed up. But all of a sudden I began to break out in a cold sweat and I got the shakes, and I got a little dizzy and I said, "Finally, it's here." I sat down to finish the rug and

Dick Tracy and hoods in an early street scene.

I couldn't do it. The pen was shaking. I told the artist, a guy by the name of Hatton, I said, "Can you finish this rug?" He said, "Sure." I went downstairs and I ordered a malted milk. I bought a cigar, I bought a package of gum, I had all this at the soda fountain and I could hardly drink the malted but I finally did get it down, and I began to calm down and went back upstairs. And this was all spontaneous—it hit me almost in a frightening sense. I said, "Surely this is not the thing I'd been looking for," but it *had* to be. So I went over and saw him. I bought a new suit, new shoes, new hat, and made the date to see Captain Patterson.

COLLINS: How was he dressed?

GOULD: When I walked in his office he gave me a cordial handshake and said, "Hello. I've got these strips with me here." He had no necktie on, he was in shirt sleeves, which was quite common for him, because I hardly ever saw him with a coat on, and he had on some old army shoes, just plain old army shoes. I remember this well because I had dressed up, and he said, with no conversation at all, he said, "Frank Tracy, Charlie Tracy . . . Dick Tracy. Let's call this guy Dick. They call cops dicks; let's call him Dick." He said, "Do you think you can have two weeks by the first of September?" Well, it was then the fifteenth of August. If he'd said, "Do you think you can have two weeks by eleven o'clock tonight," I would have said, "Sure thing!" So I got out two weeks. I hardly slept for those two weeks.

COLLINS: Didn't the Captain have some ideas about what the first story should be?

GOULD: He said, "For a starter, why don't you have him going with this girl whose father owns a delicatessen, and they live upstairs over the store. And the old man customarily takes his day's receipts in a cigar box, puts them under the bed and that night thieves start breaking into the house, and kill the old man and take the money. You take it from there." And I did. It was a whale of a start. A beautiful start.

COLLINS: Tracy wasn't a cop at the beginning of the story. Who in your mind was this guy Dick Tracy, before he was a cop? Was he wealthy, was he poor, was he an insurance guy, was he a college student . . .

GOULD: I never gave that one bit of thought.

COLLINS: Not one bit of thought?

GOULD: He was just a nice young guy.

COLLINS: Probably about twenty years old.

GOULD: Probably about, I'd say, twenty-five.

COLLINS: Maybe working in an office someplace?

GOULD: Could be. Because after the hold-up, Tracy vowed over the body of the father lying on the ground that he would never stop until he found the killer.

COLLINS: Didn't you tell me once that when Patterson told you the story, didn't you think this was a bunch of corn? Didn't you tell me you thought that was a pretty corny idea for the way the story should start; you just went along with him because he was the boss?

GOULD: Well, I never used the word *corny*. It was a good basic story.

COLLINS: You liked it from the word go?

Mrs. Pruneface.

GOULD: It was a great jump off, springboard. It was a beauty.

COLLINS: How about when he said, "Dick Tracy," and you said, "That's fine with me." Were you just going along with him or did that name sound right to you?

GOULD: I was a great guy to have simple things simple—understandable.

COLLINS: And that clicked for you?

GOULD: I was a little jealous that I didn't think of it myself. [*laughs*]

COLLINS: It was a damn good idea?

GOULD: It was a brilliant idea. Dick Tracy. Tracy was a play on tracing, in my book.

COLLINS: It was kind of a pun, but it was a real name?

GOULD: Yes.

COLLINS: Well now, in those early days of the strip, you pitted him against gangsters who were very much reflective of the gangsters who were in the news. Didn't you actually look at the news and draw on that as a source of, if not ideas, inspiration for the kinds of character that you . . . ?

GOULD: I kept up with the police reports in the newspaper, and I studied in the crime detection laboratory in Chicago, which was part of Northwestern. So I got a touch of lab work, as it was being performed for the city of Chicago. The police didn't have their own crime laboratory then. Later on it was made part of the Police Department and pulled out of Northwestern.

COLLINS: In the thirties the villains that Tracy was pitted against were very much Dillinger types. Bonnie and Clyde types. Baby Face Nelson. The kind of gangster—in Capone, Big Boy—the kind of gang-

Itchy.

Previously unpublished tryout strips for "Fillum Fun."

ster that was existing in Chicago and the Midwest and all over the country. But by the end of the thirties and the early 1940s you started pitting Tracy against a different kind of villain, a larger-than-life kind of villain. How did that evolve? How did we go from Big Boy and Cutie Diamond and Zora Arson into Pruneface and B-B Eyes?

GOULD: Because I was trying to outdo every cartoonist in the business. My theory was Stifle All Competition.

COLLINS: Who in your mind was the first of the larger-than-life villains in Tracy?

GOULD: Oh, I think one of the very first ones I had with all his pictorial possibilities was the Mole. I think he was one of the early ones.

COLLINS: I think he was 1941?

MASTERSON: Little Face, even before the Mole.

GOULD: Little Face . . . then I had . . .

MASTERSON: B-B Eyes . . .

GOULD: And a guy that looked like Edward G. Robinson . . .

COLLINS: Oh, Stooge Viller.

GOULD: Stooge Viller was Number One of a new crop. He was Number One.

COLLINS: Something unusual about Stooge Viller with Chester Gould is that you used him a number of times, and you are not one to use a villain over. Do you know how many times you used Stooge?

GOULD: No.

COLLINS: Three times. Am I correct, Matt?

MASTERSON: Yes, three.

COLLINS: And there's no other villain that I can say that about. You must have liked that guy.

GOULD: Well, I don't remember whether I liked him or not, but he must have fit into my idea of a good story.

COLLINS: I very vividly remember reading the story where Tracy, fed up with this guy, beats Stooge up in his jail cell. Do you remember what he said to him? He said, "Next time I'm going to shoot first and investigate afterwards," which is a line that has been appropriated by many, many detectives, or detective writers, I should say. You really, in the thirties, were one of the first writers—never mind cartoonists, but writers—to write about a tough detective hero. You and Dashiell Hammett and a few other people.

GOULD: I was ahead of Dashiell Hammett.

COLLINS: You were all working at about the same time, doing the same kind of thing. You popularized the idea of . . . I call it a trench coat, you call it a camel's hair coat, but you know what I mean . . . the collar and the look and the snap brim hat. Pretty soon Hollywood was picking up on your kind of hero, and by the end of the thirties and into the forties, Dick Tracy was in the movies. How did you feel about the "Dick Tracy" movie adaptations?

GOULD: I felt about it like everybody feels about the movies. They put a bunch of these little hack writers on it, and they put another writer on it, and when they got through it's worse than a committee job, it's a puzzle that's been put together. They hope it'll sell and fill the theaters. But we made good money out of it.

COLLINS: The first batch of them were serials, Saturday afternoon serials.

GOULD: Serials were first, then finally—features.

COLLINS: Did you watch all the chapters of the serials or did you just check out the first few?

GOULD: I never wrote any of the stuff—

COLLINS: Now, as far as going to them yourself, did you watch the whole thing?

GOULD: Oh, yes. I saw every one. Serials and the B-pictures they made.

COLLINS: The serials with Ralph Byrd were not very faithful to the strip, but movies that were made in the mid-forties and late forties, with first Morgan Conway and then Ralph Byrd again, tried to be pretty faithful to the spirit of the strip.

GOULD: Yes, those are what I call B-pictures. They were passably good.

COLLINS: How did you like the two men who played Tracy?

GOULD: Well, as long as the check came in, I said, "They're all right."

COLLINS: Did you like either of them, frankly?

GOULD: I don't like Hollywood's interpretation of anything. I'm prejudiced, biased. They distort anything. They even distort . . . I'm afraid to say, I think if they had tried to make a movie of the Bible—Cecil B. DeMille did several times—to me there would be a desecration when they got through with it.

COLLINS: There are a lot of people who seem to feel that Ralph Byrd was a pretty good Dick Tracy.

GOULD: Oh, I think he was, I think he was the best of the lot I saw.

COLLINS: What did you like about Byrd?

GOULD: He seemed to be a good actor.

COLLINS: Uh-huh. He had a good jaw.

GOULD: But that's a mistake that's made. You can't find any human being who will look like a cartoon character. But the things that are written to be said, and plotting that they could do, could be very authentic. I think they tried to do that with Byrd's stuff.

COLLINS: And Byrd went on to make a TV show too in the early fifties. Do you remember that?

GOULD: On Tracy?

COLLINS: Yeah, in 1951, I think. [EDITOR'S NOTE: The 1950-51 season.]

MASTERSON: I think it was the late-fifties.

COLLINS: No, it was early, real early. Byrd made one year of "Dick Tracy" TV shows. Had that slipped your mind?

GOULD: Well, I don't recall a TV show, I thought [the adaptation] was merely the movies.

COLLINS: No, there was a TV show. They did all the villains, they did Flattop, and the Mole, and B-B Eyes and The Brow . . .

GOULD: Oh, is that right?

COLLINS: And then Byrd died. He died in fifty-two or fifty-three. They only made one year of it, and then he passed away. But let's get into the forties, which some people consider to be, if not the Golden Era, the era where you really bloomed. It always seemed to me that 1944 was kind of a special year. Undoubtedly you had many great stories throughout the run of the entire strip. But the thing about 1944 that was special was that you created that one year three of your all-time famous, greatest villains. Bing bing bing. You did Flattop, undoubtedly the most famous. Then The Brow. Then Shaky. Why were you cooking so in that year? What was special about it?

GOULD: That's easy to answer. The war made The Brow.

COLLINS: And Flattop?

GOULD: And Flattop. And Shaky? That was purely a bonus I threw in.

Flattop.

Shaky.

COLLINS: You were cooking on something special . . . was Edna feeding you some kind of special spinach that year?

GOULD: Well, I tell you the kind of fodder that fed me was looking at my bank account. I tell you that's a hell of an incentive. This business has to be war. It has to be war, you have to defeat everything that's

The Brow.

in your way and is trying to take aim, spin off any glory from you, and you have to outmaneuver and outthink everybody. And I say you *have to*, that's a necessity. This is an ugly term I'm speaking of. You simply have to be better than the competition.

COLLINS: The forties were a very special period for "Dick Tracy," though. You created your famous villains; that really jelled for the first time in the forties. And you created B. O. Plenty in that era. Where did B. O. Plenty come from? He is possibly, next to Dick Tracy, your most famous character.

KIDS DON'T WANT TO WORK THESE DAYS. ALWAYS FIND SOME EXCUSE.

B. O. Plenty.

GOULD: I felt that he would be a great comic relief. People would say, "Can't Gould draw anything but these funny crooks?" And I thought, "Yeah, I'll draw a funny hillbilly guy." So I remember back in Oklahoma as I told you, a lot of these farmers looked like B. O. Plenty in the spring and then they'd get a haircut, and all, and they'd look like ordinary people, for a while.

COLLINS: Once-a-year haircuts?

GOULD: Yeah, once a year, that's all. Because my dad used to cut hair. He used to cut my grandfather's hair; he cut it every spring. Grandpa'd come in about the end of February. Dad'd take him out in the yard and sit him in a chair and cut his hair, and that had better hold him until next year.

COLLINS: Would you say that B. O. was your personal favorite character?

GOULD: No, I wouldn't, but I'd say he was my greatest type.

COLLINS: Your greatest comic achievement?

GOULD: The greatest type. B. O. Plenty was a type that I thought had more exclusive typing perhaps than any of them.

COLLINS: Now I know that you do not like to say what your favorites are. I know that you like to say that your favorite story is the one that you've just finished. But you've had some retirement now for a few years—although you've been as busy as ever with your business interests and so on. Now that you can reflect, do you have some favorites? Do you have a favorite villain?

GOULD: Well, I think that . . .

COLLINS: If you had to, if I were pinning you down . . .

GOULD: Well, if I had to be cornered I'd say The Brow was a good one. And Flattop of course. That was my big smash. This is when I started doing sketches and mailing them to myself. I had I think

about five or six envelopes, and I said, "As soon as this stuff appears in the paper, they can be thrown away." That was my whole object. If some jerk in the engraving room told some of the cartoonists that Gould's got this guy called Flattop and he looks like this, and the fellow said, "Gee, I'm going to put this in my strip, I'll get it in there before his gets there."

I was very familiar and on very good terms with a state policeman in the radio department of the Omaha State Police. I came up with this idea of this two-way wrist radio, after the war, in forty five—the war was just getting over, October. I had been called down to Allentown, Pennsylvania, where the Bell Telephone Laboratory is, where they develop all their stuff, you know. I was called down there to listen to and examine a two-way wrist radio. Well, the only "wrist" about it was the microphone on the wrist, and the speaker you carried stuffed in your front pocket. It was no more like Tracy's two-way radio than an ice-cream cone. But they had a big dinner for me, and I came back, and I made a sketch of the two-way wrist radio as I conceived it, very similar to what it is now, or what it was when I last drew it. And also, I said to this guy, "They tell me television is coming in," and he said, "Forget television. Police work on words only. What can they do with a picture? It's going to be hard enough for your readers to believe that you can get a two-way wrist radio. Television they'd laugh at—it wouldn't even be a good story." Well, he was right, I absolutely agreed with him. Anyway, I drew these two things, and mailed them to myself, and that was in October.

COLLINS: Forty-seven?

MASTERSON: Forty-five.

GOULD: October of forty-five.

COLLINS: Forty-five, wow.

GOULD: And January of forty-six, the two-way wrist radio made its appearance. It had been dropped in the snow I believe by . . . It's a little vague, but—

MASTERSON: Diet Smith's wife, Irma.

GOULD: Ohhhhh yeah . . .

MASTERSON: The actual inventor of the wrist radio was Brilliant, the blind scientist. Blind inventor. It was actually disclosed afterwards that he was Diet Smith's son.

GOULD: Oh, I see, I see. By golly, I'd forgotten all that.

COLLINS: Another thing you're famous for is your so-called death traps, or cliff-hanging situations where Tracy is in a real jam. You used that all the way through the strip, from the first years to the very end of the strip. There is a story that you've told me more than once that I'd like to get in this interview which is the one time that Gould tried to step in and save Tracy with . . . well I don't want to spoil it . . .

GOULD: You must be referring to the time that I threw Tracy down . . . a bunch of thugs threw him down . . . a caisson.

COLLINS: Yes.

GOULD: Oh, about two feet in diameter, and it's a deep hole. Well, then they rolled a stone on top of him, a hell of a big stone, and gravity was slowly pulling it through this clay, and the edge was just

Even Chester Gould had difficulty finding a way for Dick Tracy to escape this peril.

fitted enough so it didn't drop, it was going down slowly. As the stone descended, I was trying to figure out what to do. As I told you the other day, get your characters in a corner where they can't get out, and when nothing can save them, then *you* have to save them. Well . . .

COLLINS: In other words, you would get him in a jam . . . and you wouldn't know how you were getting him out?

GOULD: Oh no, that would ruin the whole thing, if I tried to figure it out. Because you would say, "Well, I wouldn't do that, it's too hard."

COLLINS: The theory being that if you don't know what's going to happen next, neither will the reader.

GOULD: That's correct. So I said, "Well, I'll do something unique in all the history of comics. I'll have Tracy say, 'Gould, you've gone too far, what can you do?' and show a hand and a piece of art gum erasing it. I thought, "Gee, this would be a first." Well, I got a call from Patterson, he said, "This last Sunday page you can't do. You'll have to redraw the finish. That will kill all your readers' faith and you won't have anything to hang on to if you do that." And I said, "Captain, I'll fix it, I'll change it," and he sent the strip, the page, back.

COLLINS: So you had to fix the thing up?

GOULD: So Tracy's heels made a hollow sound as he was stomping around and sweating blood, and he found out that he was walking on boards and the boards were part of the ceiling forming for concrete, so he managed to get the attention of one of the workmen down below, yelling, and they cut a hole out of this form, and the wood dropped down first and then Tracy dropped down, and then the stone dropped down. He was able to roll out of the way just in the nick of time. That's the way I did it.

MASTERSON: The caisson turned out to be a ventilator shaft?

GOULD: Yeah. It was a ventilator shaft for a new tunnel.

COLLINS: While we're talking about the forties—and it's a very important era in "Tracy" and probably there's a lot of things that I should touch on that I haven't touched on—but one thing that I don't think I've heard you asked about publicly was your experience in the late forties with this special promotion that didn't run in all the newspapers. Now you'll have to help me here, Matt.

MASTERSON: Oh, about "The Black Bag Mystery," which was a promotion, a circulation booster.

GOULD: Oh yeah, that was purely a circulation promotion. That was just a commercial thing like they had you recommend canned corn or something. It was something more than a recommendation, a circulation stimulant for the strip.

COLLINS: It was a special little mystery that you did, and you had some help on it.

GOULD: That was the Crystal Lake artist that came over. I would pencil the stuff in rather crudely. I didn't want this to be of the same caliber as Dick Tracy on the comics page. He was a pretty good artist, it went along real good and they asked me what I wanted for doing that—extra money—and I said, "Not one cent. My reward has been in being in the *Chicago Tribune* and they have paid me over and over but I am proud and happy to do that, it's my own paper . . ." Well, one morning the production manager of the *Trib,* John Parker, came in and said, "Patterson wants you to come over with us to the garage at 11:00 and see some new equipment." When I got there, the rest of the *Tribune* directors were there, and I said, "What the hell is this?" It was dark in the garage; I mean fairly dark, but I could see a big tar-paper thing that looked like a house, and I looked at it a second time and there was kind of a handle on it, and about that time there was a roar of a motor—a rrrroooowwwwr—and right through the paper came a Cadillac, with Colonel McCormick behind the wheel. He stepped out and said, "It's all yours." That was the kind of guy he was.

COLLINS: Was that a special moment for you, Chet?

GOULD: Very much so. Very very touching thing. McCormick was a very generous guy and very lovable fellow. He was determined to pay for that contest. They wanted to put on a hundred thousand circulation, but they did put on fifty thousand on that contest. The Colonel always said he'd pay a dollar [per thousand of new circulation] in any contest. That meant he would gladly pay fifty thousand dollars for that contest. But I had a lot of excitement and wonderful years.

COLLINS: You had a great sense of loyalty to the *Chicago Tribune*, since that's where you got your start. Were you approached by the Field people about the same time that Milton Caniff was wooed away from "Terry and the Pirates" for "Steve Canyon"?

GOULD: That's right . . .

COLLINS: You didn't buy it, did you?

GOULD: No. It had a very strange beginning and had I known the facts at the beginning I would just have told the guy not to waste his time. But I got a phone call one day and the voice said, "Mr. Gould, I'd like to see you sometime," and I said, "What about?" and he said, "I can't tell you over the phone. I'm under strict orders not to tell you and I'd like very much to talk to you either downtown or in your home, anywhere." And I was suspicious as hell. I said, "If I don't know what you want to talk to me about, I'm not about to meet you. I don't understand what it can be that you can't tell me."

And he said, "I think you'd be very happy to know—this is good news. But I cannot tell you." I was then making about forty thousand dollars or forty-five thousand dollars a year. And he called me again—the first call was downtown, the second call was downtown, the third was out here. It was a winter night; it was snowing. I'd just gotten home, I got home about quarter of seven on that train I rode, and Edna and I were having supper and the phone rang, this same guy. He said, "I'm in Woodstock, I'm the guy who's been trying to talk to you. I'm in Woodstock and I'm going to drive out to your place." I said, "Well, you can ride out if you want to, it's snowing. I have no idea what you have in mind, but if you want to come out come right ahead." So I got my .38 snubnose and hid it under the cushion of the upholstered chair we had, and when the car came in Edna said, "You stay there and I'll go see who it is." Well, it was a nice-looking fellow, well-built, apparently in his early fifties, with a camel's hair coat on, and galoshes, and she brought him in here . . . I was still sitting in the chair. He said, "My name is Smith Davis. I'm a finder for newspaper publishers on what to buy or sell. I just sold Frank Knox's *Daily News* to the next owner, Jack Knight. I have a message from Mr. [Marshall] Field [of the *Sun-Times*]."

By this time Edna was hanging up his coat, and he was walking in, and I got up and said, "Well, I don't know you, but you look to me like you're a very, very brave guy to come this far in a snowstorm." He said, "It'd never have happened this way, Mr. Gould, if I'd had my way, but I was under orders from Mr. Field. He wants to hire you away from the *Tribune*." I said, "Gee, that's right interesting." And he said [Field] was ready to offer a hundred thousand dollar guarantee. "We've got Caniff. He's going to leave the *Tribune.*" I said, "Well, I'm not leaving the *Tribune.*"

He said, "Well, that's up to you. I took an oath I would follow through on this, Field wants Caniff and you." I said, "You tell Mr. Field, give him a big thank you—you tell him I'm working for the outfit that gave me the only break that I've had in my life. And a million dollars wouldn't get me away." He said, "I love that kind of talk, I appreciate it," and stuck his hand out. I said, "You need a drink," and he said, "*Do* I need a drink."

So we went into the little bar, I put out a bottle of Grandad, a brand-new bottle. I said, "Pour your own drink." He took a six-ounce straight-up glass that I had, about that high, and about so big around, and he poured it up about that far from the top with bourbon and took a big slug and a little water, and another slug, and we talked—we talked about the country out here and my early history with the *Trib,* and pretty soon he said, "You don't know how relieved I am. This has been a battle. I tried to convince Field that if I did it my way, we'd have it done weeks ago, but, no, he didn't want any word to go out over the phone." Smith Davis was his name, and I found out he was a tremendous big shot in the brokerage newspaper and bartering papers.

MASTERSON: That would have been 1946, '47?

GOULD: Yes. The war was just winding down or had wound down.

COLLINS: Chet, I'm assuming that they would have wanted you to do a strip similar to "Dick Tracy," perhaps about another detective who was like Dick Tracy. Did you, in addition to your loyalty to the *Tribune,* have any sense that possibly lightning might not strike again? Did you have a sense that "Dick Tracy" was your vehicle and you wanted to say with it?

GOULD: No. My thinking about the *Tribune* dominated everything—I would be a traitor.

COLLINS: I see.

GOULD: In my mind I would have been a traitor, I would have done everything that was considered evil in my book.

COLLINS: Well, let me come up one more time around on the other side of this. Wouldn't you agree that a "Dick Tracy" can only be created once? That it is difficult for someone, no matter how brilliant, to create another Tarzan or another Sherlock Holmes, or another Dick Tracy?

GOULD: Well, I think I've got what you're talking about now. I think, had I been fired for some reason, or was on the verge of losing my job . . . I think then I could then have gone out and done another "Dick Tracy" under another name. [*EDITOR'S NOTE: Gould on previous occasions often said that he believed Tracy was his "gold mine" and doubted a second similar strip, even by him, could have had as big an impact.*]

COLLINS: I have just a couple more questions for you, because I think we should wind this up. And then if Matt has anything he wants to touch on that we haven't touched on, I'll turn this over to him. You worked with a number of assistants but some

of them went on to do other things. Your first assistant was Dick Moores; is that correct?

GOULD: Yes.

COLLINS: Or he was one of the first in the thirties. Who were some of your other assistants over the years?

GOULD: Well there was Dick Moores, then there was, oh . . .

MASTERSON: Russell Stamm?

GOULD: Russell Stamm.

COLLINS: Who went on to do "Invisible Scarlet O'Neil."

GOULD: Yes.

COLLINS: Did Stamm do good work for you?

GOULD: He couldn't draw a straight line when he came with me, and his cousin Stanley Link [*EDITOR'S NOTE: Link had assisted on "The Gumps" and later drew "Tiny Tim."*] tutored him and I went along with him, and he learned to rule and letter—no figures —but he did all my lettering eventually. He was a guy who was too anxious for his own good. He stayed with me two or three years. He went over to Field with this "Invisible Scarlet O'Neil." I said to him, "You're going to have an awful hard time drawing an invisible character. What does it look like?" And of course—

COLLINS: Kind of like "Sawdust," huh?

"Sawdust"—Chester Gould's satire on modern, simplistic humor strips.

MASTERSON: Or "Invisible Tribes"? [*EDITOR'S NOTE: These refer to strips-within-the-strip in "Tracy"—both of which spoof the drawing of modern humor strips.*]

GOULD: Basically, he was a nice boy, he was just overambitious to get there quick. Then there was Locher . . .

COLLINS: Dick Locher, who is now an editorial cartoonist. [*EDITOR'S NOTE: Since the interview, Dick Locher has joined Collins to produce the modern-day "Dick Tracy."*]

GOULD: Dick Locher, and then right after Locher came Rick Fletcher.

COLLINS: You only—I'm trying to think—you really only had one lettering man over the years, other than your assistants, and that was your brother Ray. There's a great story which I've heard, but I'd like to get it on tape, about how Ray became your lettering man.

GOULD: Well, he was over in the South Pacific.

MASTERSON: New Guinea.

GOULD: New Guinea. And it was quite common that the boys would get these big coconuts with the whiskers on. About the size of a man's head, or bigger. They would letter, either with fountain pen, or any ink they could get, they would letter the address, and all they had to do was get stamps on that coconut, and they would deliver the coconut, right to the post office. And that's the way we got a coconut from Ray. But he had hand-lettered it with white paint, he got a hold of some white paint. And beautiful lettering! I thought he'd had some kind of professional guy in the service letter it for him. And when he came back here after he'd mustered out, we had that coconut on the floor. I said, "Who put that lettering on there for you?" He said, "I did." I said, "Well, geez, that's damn good lettering. Do some samples on a piece of Bristol Board, and let me see it." And he did; I gave him some pens. That's the way he got in.

COLLINS: Now, his background was in printing, like your father had been a printer.

GOULD: Yeah, Ray had been a Linotype operator and that's where he learned the shaping of the letters—what they looked like and what they should look like.

COLLINS: So he worked with you from the late forties, mid to late, on through until . . . well, really, until just a few years ago, until he died.

GOULD: Yeah.

COLLINS: You and he were very close, and you thought very highly of the work he did.

GOULD: He was a great guy. He was a real credit to this business. Ray was a quiet fellow and he was very capable. And I tried to coach him in art, and kind of carried on a little school for him, but he didn't take to drawing. It just wasn't in him, he didn't have the drawing desire, nor the ability to follow through. So he just did the lettering, and he colored the photostats of the Sunday pages, and he ruled out the Sunday pages and the daily strips, which in itself takes a lot of time. So we had a happy situation.

COLLINS: I have a question that's asked me a lot, since I live in Muscatine, Iowa, which is a small town in the midwest. And I'm now writing the story of Dick Tracy, big-city police officer, and I'm constantly asked, "Why do you live in Muscatine, Iowa?" I'm wondering why did you live in Woodstock, Illinois, for all those years? Why not on the East Coast, or why not in Chicago? What brought you to a farm?

GOULD: I have the most practical reason that you ever heard. We had a big Depression in 1929. The economists, the financial advisors, all of the business people commented on it, and said, "Get yourself a farm. When the next depression comes, at least you can eat. You can raise vegetables and meat." And I have a very good friend, Al Lowenthal, who was my agent for years. Al bought himself a farm up near Waukegan. And he bought another one over near Merringo.

COLLINS: Excuse me for interrupting, but wasn't Lowenthal the inspiration for Sam Catchem?

GOULD: Yes, yes.

COLLINS: Visually.

GOULD: Al told me, "You ought to have a Jewish detective in there," so I did. Anyway . . .

COLLINS: He'd bought the farm up near Merringo.

GOULD: He had the two places he had bought, and I said, "Where should we go, Al?" He said, "Get a farm. When the Depression comes, there'll be another one. You should have a farm and have milk and eggs and things for your table." I said, "Where should I go?" "Go to Woodstock; there's a nice little place out in the valley east of Woodstock."

So we went to Woodstock, looked up the guy and we bought this place. It was all tumbled-down, it was a mess. These were all abandoned farms out here, because it's all gravel. The families, the fellows that owned it, they just couldn't make a living on these farms. And there were broken-down houses, and windows smashed and everything. We bought the thing, and we loved the hills, and Edna thought it was beautiful and so did I. It's a very good story that follows up on that.

The good farmland in Woodstock was west and north of town. It was all flat. About the second time I was in the First National Bank, on the square, I saw a man come out from an office on the corner of the bank as I left. And he said, "I'm Frank Green, president of the First National Bank. I think you're Chester Gould, our new blood out here." I said yes. He said, "Why did you buy in that damn valley?" I said, "We thought it was beautiful out there and we're going to put in a dairy and we are now constructing a barn, corn cribs, milk house, chicken house. We're putting in the works." He said, "You'll never raise a damn thing in that gravel. It's no good. You should have bought north or west of town." I said, "Gee, I feel terrible about that. You're making me feel pretty bad, Mr. Green." He said, "I know nobody told you but it's too late now, do the best you can with it. But that is not farmland." I said, "We like what's there, we've got a little brook down there to water the cattle and everything." That ended the conversation. We later got acquainted pretty well. So one evening Edna and I were having dinner at a little restaurant called the Lily Pond. And Edna had met Mrs. Green through the hospital, they were very active in the hospital. And as we were leaving the restaurant, the Greens were coming in, right at the door. We stopped just inside the door and went through the ritual, well, "You Look Fine," "The Food's Good," "Don't Eat Yourself Out of Shape," that kind of stuff. Finally he took me by the sleeve and said, "Come over here, I want to talk to you." I thought, "What the hell is he going to say to me now? What have I done?" He said, "Do you remember [what] I told you about that acreage you bought?" "Yes." "Well, I'll tell you, you've got the damnedest, most expensive acreage in the country." [*laughter*].

COLLINS: I bet when he said that, you liked it, because he'd admitted it.

GOULD: They were too close to the forest to see the trees, which is common in a lot of cases.

COLLINS: Now one other story I'd like to pry out of you relating to this idea of the Depression and trying to make sure you can survive. You once told me a story about actually butchering a calf or cow.

GOULD: Oh yeah, well, we decided to have our own beef one year during the war, when meat was rationed, and you couldn't get it with ration coupons sometimes. So we had the only cattle that we fed up. And a farmer that did yard work for me at times said, "I'll help you butcher it." Well, we had a refrigerated house down here that Edna's brothers set up for us, and we had hooks in there on scaffolding and everything. So I got a hold of Fleming, the old-timer came over. And he said, "You get up on that sawhorse." I had a .38 revolver. He said, "Shoot this animal and when it drops I'll cut its throat." And that's what happened. He had arranged a pulley, and we put these hooks through the leaders right back here and the hind legs, and pulled it up. It was dead, of course. We skinned it and cleaned it and gutted it, and we hung it in our little cold house for about a week. There was a freezer, a commercial freezer built in Woodstock, where we got a drawer and we got hold of the butcher in town, the meat man. I said, "Will you give me a diagram of an animal with all the cuts, the meat cuts?" He said, "Sure, I got one right here, take it along," and I said, "We'll butcher our own beef," and he said, "Well, good luck."

I bought a couple of meat saws and on this given morning I went out and carried half a steer in. Edna and I had our white enamel-top kitchen table, laid it on there and, using the diagrams of the animal, we began to cut up the different cuts. With saw and butcher knife we got both of those beef halves cut into their proper cuts, eight o'clock that night. We went twelve hours around the clock cutting that beef. The locker stayed open all hours, and as we finished we took the cuts in and put them in the drawer. Filled the drawer right up. There were 104 cuts of meat on that animal. But the chart he gave me shows just one side, so the other side would have to be reversed. I stood this in front of a mirror to orient myself on the other half. We had that beef . . . that was our emergency beef until we could buy meat again.

COLLINS: Wasn't there bone dust on the floor?

GOULD: Bone dust, pieces and chips of meat. Brother, it was a mess.

COLLINS: Well, scarce as meat was, it still seems like a strange idea that here's one of the top cartoonists in the country, incredibly well paid, and he's carving up a cow. Now there had to be more motivation to it than just the scarcity of meat.

GOULD: Well, there was just absolute egotism and pride!

COLLINS: To show that you could do it and you could survive.

GOULD: And we did, we butchered our own animal and cut it up ready for the table.

COLLINS: It gave you a feeling of self-sufficiency.

GOULD: It's like any other advancement people make in their lives. You venture and you succeed and you're happy and you know you've got that in your mental bank, you've got that, "You can do it."

Mrs. GOULD: I want to tell you something. There aren't many men who will take care of their families such as Chet. And now if it gets to the point where there was no meat, the people who didn't do what Chet did, they wouldn't have meat. They'd beg for meat. We didn't have to beg for anything.

GOULD: That's right.

Mrs. GOULD: Chet takes care of his family, he doesn't have to go to anyone and say, "Oh I know you have meat, would you let me have just one pound." No, other people who never take care of themselves would have to do that, if they did it at all.

GOULD: We never complain about anything that we can help ourselves.

Mrs. GOULD: Oh, I think it's great. That's why Chet has succeeded in everything he has done. Nothing daunts him.

COLLINS: That's a good conclusion [To Matt:] Do you have any questions?

GOULD: [to Mrs. Gould] Thank you, mom.

MASTERSON: Well, I think we touched on everything except Tracy going to the Moon, Chet.

GOULD: I think that, still, that was one of the greatest series that I ever did and I'm very proud of it. I figured out that if you can travel 300 miles a day, you can circle the moon in any temperature you want, but its terrain is such that you'd almost have to use an aircar or something to do it. And you can subsist on the moon with just a little help from a container of oxygen, you don't have to go in the big iron-clad refrigerated suit with all the monkey business.

And another thing, you talk about commercial space flight. They'll never do it until they've been able to build some artificial gravity in a vehicle like an airplane or a space coupe or whatever. People cannot say, "Gee, we're going to the Moon this afternoon, and get there at half past four." They'll get there, but they'll be in a sorry condition, because when you go through weightlessness, you don't have any control. Anything can happen. And that's not going to make a whole lot of people anxious to go to the Moon.

Mrs. GOULD: Like the airplaces that were not pressurized, and many people became deaf or had a hearing problem after flying. Anything can be overcome, even weightlessness in space.

GOULD: Yes, that weightlessness has to be overcome.

Mrs. GOULD: And it will be. Men can do anything.

MASTERSON: Chet, when you first came out here, you described the house as being pretty beat up. I have a mental picture of Sunny Dell Acres.

GOULD: Well, it wasn't even as nice looking as Sunny Dell Acres.

MASTERSON: Does Sunny Dell Acres exist somewhere?

GOULD: I got that whole idea from Arlington, the town of Arlington, as you go by on the train where we first came out here—not now. It's all built up now. When we first came out here there was a little real estate office, with posts. They weren't leaning like B.O.'s. They were posts in front of the door to the real estate office. It was twisted posts and it was stucco, with a tile roof. Very much like B.O.'s place—that's where I got the idea for that. And that was there—we came out in thirty-five—that was there until after the war. And then that subdivision that hadn't been built up at all, it just had a couple of stone gates at every entrance. There were several entrances to it, and they had these stone gates. That's where I got that.

MASTERSON: We've run through all your years with Dick Tracy. What's Chester Gould doing today? Now that you're not doing "Dick Tracy"?

GOULD: I did a cartoon for the [local] hospital; they're going to have some sort of a television show and they want me to moderate that, discussing the hospital drive. They want to raise three million dollars for the local hospital.

MASTERSON: So you're keeping your hand and mind active, and you're keeping samples ready if the time should come?

GOULD: I've never been so active in my life.

COLLINS: Well, "Check-Out Chickie" is one of sev-eral new strips that you've been developing since you left "Dick Tracy." Do you have any plans to get back into the cartooning business full time?

GOULD: Never. Never. I went through that rat race long enough.

COLLINS: So then your new projects are designed to be possibly sold to a syndicate or turned over to—

GOULD: I want to sell ideas and I want to contribute individual cartoons for causes and charitable things, and I want to keep active.

COLLINS: All right. Anything else, Matt?

MASTERSON: We can spread the news that if any-one's looking for a good idea, we can give them your phone number.

COLLINS: Right.

[*all laugh*]

ENTER LIZZ

PRINCIPAL PERPETRATORS: **Joe Period;
Flattop, Jr.; Ivy**

ORIGINALLY APPEARED: January 1, 1956–
December 24, 1956
WRITER/ARTIST: Chester Gould

Chester Gould remained capable of imaginative storytelling—wild action, crazy villains, stylish artwork—until the very end. But the rigors of creating a comic strip, over a forty-seven-year period, meant that even with Chester Gould at the helm, the quality of stories would vary. Even Babe Ruth didn't hit the ball out of the park *every* time he stepped up to the plate.

Now and then, though, Chester Gould would really pull out the stops; inspiration and hard work would converge in a brilliant sustained run: a year that was consistently terrific. One of those was 1944, when the three principal villains were Flattop, The Brow, and Shaky . . . in three of the best "Tracy" stories ever. Another was 1950—showcasing villains Wormy (who disrupted Tracy's honeymoon); Flattop's revenge-seeking brother Blowtop; and the despicable T. V. Wiggles, who nearly killed sweet little Sparkle Plenty.

Yet another such year was 1956, which is presented here in its virtual entirety. Usually when "Tracy" volumes have been produced, stories have been plucked from this year and that. One of Gould's many strengths was his day-to-day continuity, and the manner in which one story flowed into, and converged with, another. We decided it was about time readers got a jolt of pure Gould— the sustained stellar performance of one of his greatest years.

Hoody, black-leather-jacketed, rock-and-roll-influenced Joe Period is a classic juvenile delinquent, revealing Gould's finger on the pop-culture pulse; and Joe's fellow j.d., Flattop, Jr., is a worthy successor to his evil father. Flattop's Jr.'s gadget-laden car, incidentally, has been said to have influenced the similar car in the James Bond film *Goldfinger.*

Gould was particularly brave in the Flattop, Jr., continuity, playing by his own rules and no one else's: is the "ghost" clinging to Flattop, Jr.'s neck the boy's conscience? Or *literally* the spirit of a murder victim? The answer, ultimately, is surprising.

If counterfeiter Ivy is a less memorable villain than Joe Period or Flattop, Jr., his tale allows Gould to reveal his mastery of the medium in an evocative, expressionistic sequence involving a cliff, the sea, and sharks. It's a twisting story rich in character and surprising turns of plot, completing what was probably the single best year of Gould's later career. Perhaps significantly, 1956 marked the twenty-fifth anniversary of "Dick Tracy."

But all in all, despite the presence of Flattop, Jr., 1956 is policewoman Lizz's year. Long before Angie Dickinson, way before women's lib, Lizz was a tough cop who was a match for any fiendish foe. In this, her introductory year, Lizz is involved in training that shows Gould effectively incorporating the up-to-the-minute police procedure that is a "Dick Tracy" hallmark.

I TOLD YOU I WAS NO GOOD AT PLAYING CUPID. SHE SAID FOR YOU TO QUIT BOTHERING HER.

WHAT?

SHE SAID YOU WERE THREE TIMES HER AGE—

—AND HERE'S THAT 100 BUCKS YOU PAID ME. I'M GIVING IT BACK. I DIDN'T EARN IT.

KEEP IT, JOE PERIOD. YOU DID THE BEST YOU COULD. IT WASN'T YOUR FAULT.

GEE, THANKS, MR. POCKETCLIP.

WELL, I'LL BE GOING. IF YOU WANT ME, LET ME KNOW. GLAD TO WORK FOR YOU ANY TIME, MR. POCKETCLIP.

LATER AT THE STAGE DOOR OF CLUB PAREE.

GOODNIGHT, MISS MARRLIN.

GOODNIGHT, EDDIE.

WHAT?

YEAH— IT'S ME AGAIN.

I DELIVERED YOUR MESSAGE, AND THEN I GOT TO FIGURING MAYBE I WAS MORE YOUR TYPE. HOW ABOUT HAVING A SANDWICH WITH ME?

OH, BROTHER! YOU NERVY KIDS!

GOOD NIGHT, NOW— AHA, HA! HA!

YEAH?

AND AT POLICE HEADQUARTERS

WORKING LATE TONIGHT, AREN'T YOU, LIZZ?

YES, I RECEIVED MY NOTIFICATION FROM CIVIL SERVICE TO APPEAR TOMORROW, AND I'M SORT OF BRUSHING UP.

CHESTER GOULD

YOU'LL FIND THIS WORK DIFFERENT FROM ANYTHING ELSE YOU'VE EVER KNOWN.

I'M SURE OF THAT, MR. TRACY.

THAT CLIPPING! JUST WHAT INTEREST DOES IT HOLD FOR LIZZ?

IN THE ROLE OF CUPID, JOE PERIOD FAILS—AND REPORTS THAT FACT TO LOVESICK MR. POCKETCLIP. BUT IS JOE ON THE LEVEL?

WHAT A DISH!

SO THAT'S WHERE SHE LIVES!

CALLED ME A JUVENILE. LAUGHED AT ME. SAID I WAS A NERVY KID.

YEAH? THAT'S WHAT SHE THINKS! I COULD SEE IT IN HER EYES—SHE LIKES ME. —LIKES ME A LOT.

WHAT? WHY, THAT'S POCKETCLIP HIMSELF! I JUST LEFT HIM A LITTLE BIT AGO!—AND HE'S GOING IN THERE—

CHESTER GOULD

LOVESICK MR. POCKETCLIP DECIDES TO MAKE ONE LAST PLEA.

I LOVE HER—I CAN'T LIVE WITHOUT HER—I'LL TELL HER SO IF I HAVE TO YELL IT THROUGH THE KEYHOLE.

WHO'S THERE?

GET AWAY FROM HERE AND **LEAVE ME ALONE!**

JULIE, LONG BEFORE YOU MARRIED "DUCKY," I LOVED YOU! IT WASN'T MY FAULT HE WENT TO THE CHAIR—NO LAWYER COULD HAVE SAVED HIM. LISTEN TO ME, JULIE—

SLAM!

TELL ME YOU'LL GIVE ME A CHANCE, JULIE, OR I'LL—I'LL PULL THE TRIGGER.

UH—UH—

YOU! WHAT ARE YOU DOING HERE?

I WON'T LET YOU SHOOT YOURSELF, MR. POCKETCLIP—SHE DOESN'T LOVE YOU, AND THAT'S THAT.

AHA—I SEE IT ALL NOW—YOU DOUBLE-CROSSER! **YOU'RE AFTER HER YOURSELF!**

SO WHAT?

YOU TREACHEROUS LITTLE JUVENILE—**I'LL KILL YOU!**

STAY AWAY FROM THAT GUN, MR. POCKETCLIP!

STAY AWAY FROM THAT GUN!

WHAT DID YOU DO TO HIM?—**EEK!**

SOMEBODY MUST HAVE PHONED THE COPS! THE HOUSE DICKS ARE COMING UP THE HALL—I CAN'T GET OUT—

STAY AWAY FROM THAT DOOR, AND SEE THAT YOU DON'T YELL.

AREN'T YOU THE CUTE ONE? **NOW**, WHAT DO WE DO?

---A DEAD MAN--- IN THE THIRD FLOOR HALL OF THE COPA APARTMENTS---

—COPA APARTMENTS—THAT'S ON LAKE DRIVE. A VERY SNOOTY PLACE.

YEAH? AND THE DETAILS?

—FLOWERS AND CANDY STREWN AROUND A WELL-DRESSED CORPSE. THAT'S ALL WE GOT.

LOVELY, LOVELY! —GUN THIS THING!

COPA APARTMENTS—THAT'S WHERE **SHE** LIVES.

YES, CHIEF—IT'S PAUL POCKETCLIP—A DISBARRED ATTORNEY. I REMEMBER HIM WELL. HE SERVED TIME FOR JURY TAMPERING.

NO VISIBLE WOUNDS ON THE BODY.

HE MUST HAVE HAD A HEART ATTACK.

FLOWERS—A BOX OF CANDY. THIS MAN WAS CALLING ON A LADY FRIEND.

THE SHOE LACE?

YEAH.

WHAT KIND OF AN APARTMENT HOTEL IS THIS?

VERY HIGH CLASS, ONE OF THE BEST ON THE NORTH SIDE.

I CAN SEE YOU'RE NOT CONVINCED IT WAS A HEART ATTACK, TRACY.

WHAT DO YOU THINK, CORONER?

WELL, SHALL WE START KNOCKING ON DOORS TO SEE IF ANYONE HEARD A COMMOTION.

LET'S LOOK AROUND FIRST, SAM.

SUDDENLY, SOMETHING PROTRUDING FROM THE BOTTOM OF A DOOR CATCHES TRACY'S EYE. HE GRASPS IT AND PULLS.

THIS DOOR, SAM.

YES, THAT'S RIGHT. JULIE MARRLIN, THE SINGER. WHAT CAN I DO FOR YOU GENTLEMEN?

MISS MARRLIN, WOULD YOU BE KIND ENOUGH TO ANSWER A FEW QUESTIONS?

HIM? I-I NEVER SAW HIM BEFORE IN MY LIFE—WHEN DID THIS HAPPEN?

DID YOU HEAR ANYTHING IN THE HALL?

HOW COULD I? I WAS ASLEEP.

YES—I WAS ASLEEP.

YOU HEARD NO NOISE—IN THE HALL?

I DIDN'T HEAR A THING TILL YOU KNOCKED ON MY DOOR.

THE REASON WE KNOCKED— THIS PIECE OF SHOELACE WAS CAUGHT IN YOUR DOOR.

SHOELACE? I'M SURE I DON'T UNDERSTAND.

AS SAM AND THE OFFICERS CAME DOWN THE ALLEY, JOE PERIOD ROLLED UNDER THE CAR TO THE SIDE OF THE BUILDING—

—AND KICKED HIS WAY THROUGH THIS BASEMENT WINDOW.

THIS IS MERELY A BAGGAGE STORE-ROOM—FOR GUESTS' TRUNKS, ETC., AS YOU CAN SEE.

THESE OPENINGS AT THE CEILING—WHAT ARE THEY?

AT ONE TIME A CONVEYER BELT PASSED THROUGH THIS ROOM. IT WAS USED TO CARRY PROVISIONS FROM A LOADING PLATFORM TO THE HOTEL KITCHEN.

A LABYRINTH OF BEAMS AND PIPES.

HE HAD TO CRAWL UP THERE—THIS DOOR WAS LOCKED.

THERE'S A LONG ROW OF UPRIGHT BEAMS WITH SPACES WHERE HE COULD HAVE ASCENDED.

MEANWHILE, AT THE EMERGENCY WARD, THE CORONER TALKS TO TRACY—

THE BULLET THAT KILLED THE PARAKEET ALSO STRUCK THE GIRL.

WHERE IS SHE?

LIZZ! WHAT ARE YOU DOING HERE? YOU'RE NOT ON ACTIVE DUTY—YET.

WHERE IS SHE? WHERE IS THE SINGER, JULIE MARRLIN?

WE WERE SEPARATED AT THE ORPHANAGE FOURTEEN YEARS AGO. ONLY IN RECENT MONTHS DID WE LEARN EACH OTHER'S IDENTITY— THIS GIRL IS MY SISTER!

MEANWHILE, SOMEWHERE IN THE STEEL-WEB OF THE HOTEL STRUCTURE—

I'M LOST---WHICH ONE DID I COME UP?

YES, SHE IS MY SISTER.

I WAS TEN AND SHE WAS ELEVEN WHEN WE WERE TAKEN FROM THE ORPHANAGE.

WHEN NEXT I HEARD OF HER —EIGHT YEARS LATER—SHE WAS MARRIED TO A MEMBER OF THE UNDERWORLD.

I BEGGED HER TO GIVE HIM UP —BUT SHE HAD A BEAUTIFUL VOICE—AND HE BOOKED HER INTO NIGHT CLUBS—SO—

36

JOE PERIOD, WE KNOW YOU'RE HID IN THOSE STEEL GIRDERS SOMEWHERE!

WE'RE GIVING YOU FIVE MINUTES TO SURRENDER.

IF WE DON'T SEE YOU OR HEAR YOUR VOICE WITHIN FIVE MINUTES, WE'RE FILLING THESE PASSAGES WITH TEAR GAS.
MEOW

THERE ARE LOTS OF RATS IN THESE WALLS—I HEARD 'EM. THAT'S WHAT BRINGS YOU HERE, EH, KITTEN?
MEOW

YOU'RE COLD AND WET. THAT MEANS YOU HAVE ACCESS TO THE OUTDOORS.

IF I CAN FOLLOW YOU, I CAN GET OUT OF HERE.

OKAY— SCAT, CAT! SCAT!

GET GOING— BEAT IT!

HERE IT COMES—

WITH THE FIRST WHIFF OF GAS, THE CAT BOLTS.

EASY, CAT! YI! DON'T BREAK THAT YARN!

MEANWHILE, LIZZ AND SAM ARE PHOTOGRAPHING FINGERPRINTS IN THE DEAD GIRL'S APARTMENT.
TO THINK THAT MY FIRST CASE INVOLVES CATCHING THE MURDERER OF MY OWN SISTER.

WITH THE FIRST WHIFF OF TEAR GAS, THE CAT TAKES OFF—

BETTER GIVE 'IM ANOTHER.

EYES BURN---I CAN'T SEE ---BUT I CAN FOLLOW THE YARN.

THE CAT LED HIM OUT.

THEN HE JUMPED IN THAT SOUPED-UP JALOPY AND LEFT OUR SQUAD CAR LIKE IT WAS STANDING STILL.

LIZZ AND I GOT EXCELLENT FINGER-PRINTS FROM THE WINDOW OF THE DEAD GIRL'S ROOM, BUT WE DON'T HAVE A PICTURE OF JOE PERIOD IN OUR FILES.

"WHERE IS LIZZ?" ASKS TRACY. "SHE'S WITH JUNIOR, IN YOUR OFFICE."

I'M THE ONLY ONE WHO REALLY CAME FACE TO FACE WITH JOE PERIOD, AND SINCE THE DEPARTMENT HAS NO PICTURES OF HIM, I'M HELPING JUNIOR.

YOU KNOW, TRACY, I READ IN ONE OF YOUR CRIMINOLOGY BOOKS THAT A CLAY MODEL IS MORE EFFECTIVE FOR IDENTI-FICATION PURPOSES THAN A SKETCH.

TRUE, JUNIOR. THE SKETCH IS QUICKER, BUT THE CLAY MODEL IS MORE COMPRE-HENSIVE! YOU GET ALL THE VARIOUS DIMENSIONS.

WOULD YOU HAVE SOMEONE GET US A BLACK LEATHER JACKET, SO WE CAN DRESS THE MODEL BEFORE IT'S PHOTOGRAPHED.

HIS HAIR—IT WAS SHORTER ON TOP AND MORE WOOLY, JUNIOR.

THAT'S ANOTHER ADVANTAGE OF A CLAY MODEL, JUNIOR, THE WITNESSES CAN HELP RECREATE THE LIKENESS.

AHA! —NOW, THE EYEBROWS— JUST A LITTLE HIGHER—

"NOTHING" YONSON'S OFFICE

CRACKED UP MY CAR—GOT NO PLACE ELSE TO GO—

YES, LIZZ, SINCE YOU'RE THE ONLY ONE WHO'S SEEN HIM, YOUR WORD WILL BE FINAL.

IT'S VERY GOOD.

I CAN PUT MY FULL STAMP OF APPROVAL ON THIS LIKENESS OF JOE PERIOD.

GOOD! NOW, TAKE YOUR COLORS, JUNIOR AND FLESH-TINT IT AND BLACK THE HAIR—THEN WE'LL PUT THE JACKET ON IT AND PHOTOGRAPH IT.

B-BUT HOW DID YOU GET HERE —FROM THE WRECK?

I STOLE A PARKED TAXICAB.

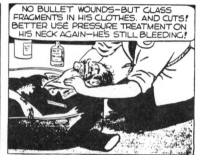

43

44

HI, SHERIFF! DID WE BEAT THE FREIGHT?

BY OVER HALF AN HOUR.

IT'S ONLY A TEN-MINUTE DRIVE TO THE YARDS, SO EVEN IF THAT FREIGHT TRAIN IS ON TIME—WE'LL HAVE FIFTEEN MINUTES TO GET READY.

ANOTHER YOKEL TOWN—AND THEY'RE SLOWING DOWN.

GOT TO SHAKE THIS TUB AND GET SOME DECENT CLOTHES AND SOME GRUB.

NO—IT CAN'T BE!

HALT!

ZING

I'M AT THE EAST END OF THE YARDS, SAM. HE CRAWLED UNDER A CAR.

KETTLES ARE FULL. BETTER HOLD UP AWHILE, JACK.

HE CLOSED THE HATCH! WHAT IS THIS? WHAT AM I IN? BR-BR-BR—!

NOPE—DIDN'T SEE A SOUL AROUND HERE.

BRINE! PICKLES AND BRINE! BR-BR—

—AND COLD! BR-RR—

HAVE YOU BEEN OUT HERE ALL THE TIME?

PRACTICALLY SO. I WAS INSIDE THE PLANT FOR A FEW MINUTES, BUT I DIDN'T SEE ANYONE PASS HERE.

BRINE AND CUCUMBERS— WHAT A PICKLE! OW! — AND LOOK AT THIS!

WE SAW KIDS AT THE OTHER END OF THE YARD, TRACY. MAYBE YOU MISTOOK ONE OF THOSE FOR JOE.

NO. I SAW JOE.

47

WE HAD BAGGED A COUPLE OF RABBITS BACK IN THAT CORN FIELD WHEN WE HEARD THE DOG BAY—

NO FOOTPRINTS EXCEPT OURS—HE MUST HAVE FALLEN FROM THE TRESTLE OR FROM A TRAIN.

WHAT'S THAT IN HIS HAND?

HE'S CLUTCHING A NEWSPAPER.

JUST A BUM—APPARENTLY FELL OFF THE TRAIN—WE'LL TAKE HIM TO THE MORGUE.

MEANWHILE, BACK IN THE FREIGHT YARDS.

HOW DID JOE PERIOD DO IT? WHERE DID HE GO?

WE'VE FOUND THE CAR HE WAS RIDING IN, TRACY.

BOTTLES—BANDAGES—ALL KINDS OF JUNK.

HARDWARE FROM THE OTHER HALF OF THE FIDDLE CASE—IN THOSE ASHES. HE MUST HAVE BURNED THE CASE FOR FUEL.

HEY, BOYS, IT APPEARS JOE PERIOD WASN'T ALONE.

PIECE OF TIN

WHAT DO YOU MEAN, TRACY?

A PAIR OF CHEAP READING GLASSES AND A LOWER PLATE, ON THE LEDGE UNDER THIS TOWEL.

MAYBE THAT FIGURE YOU SAW DASH BETWEEN THE FREIGHT CARS WAS THE OWNER OF THESE —AND NOT JOE PERIOD.

NO, I RECOGNIZED JOE'S JACKET, AND HE WAS TOO AGILE FOR AN OLD MAN.

MEANWHILE, THE PICKLE VATS HAVING BEEN EMPTIED WHILE JOE STOOD UNOBSERVED KNEE DEEP IN BRINE, THE HATCH IS AGAIN CLOSED AND THE CAR IS SHUNTED TO A SIDING.

AND THE COLD MARCH NIGHT DESCENDS—

CHESTER GOULD

SHUNTED TO A SIDING, THE PICKLE CAR IS LEFT UNTIL SUCH TIME AS IT WILL BE CLEANED AND SENT BACK TO THE CUCUMBER COUNTRY.

I CAN'T STAND THIS ANY LONGER! I'VE GOT TO GIVE UP! HELP!

I CAN ALMOST TOUCH THE HATCH COVER—BUT WHAT GOOD WOULD THAT DO ME? WITH ONLY ONE ARM, I COULDN'T PULL MYSELF UP.

CHESTER GOULD

THE BODY'S BEING PICKED UP NOW. THE CHIEF THOUGHT YOU MIGHT LIKE TO VIEW IT.

SUPPOSE IT'S JOE PERIOD?

COULD BE THE OWNER OF THIS LOWER PLATE AND THE READING GLASSES.

49

TRACY AND THE SHERIFF NOW VIEWING A BODY PICKED UP UNDER THE RAILROAD TRESTLE. SEARCH OF THE FREIGHT YARDS STILL GOING ON.

NO IDENTIFICATION ON HIM, BUT THE LOWER DENTURE YOU FOUND IN THE BOXCAR FITS HIS MOUTH.

THIS PAPER CLUTCHED IN HIS HAND—THE FOOTPRINT ON HIS COAT—THERE'S LITTLE QUESTION ABOUT IT—THIS WAS JOE PERIOD'S COMPANION AND HE WAS PUSHED TO HIS DEATH.

AND BACK TO JOE PERIOD

I HEARD SOMETHING!

AT LAST! SOMEBODY'S OPENING THE HATCH.

THERE'S SOMEBODY IN THERE, ALL RIGHT, MISS, 'CAUSE WE HEARD 'EM YELL AND MOAN.

JUST A MINUTE TILL I GET MY FLASHLIGHT.

HELLO, HELLO!

HUH? A GIRL?

NO KIDDING! JOE PERIOD HIMSELF!

YOU?

TRACY WILL BE DELIGHTED TO HEAR ABOUT THIS—JOE PERIOD PICKLED!

FOR AN INSTANT LIZZ'S SCARF COMES WITHIN JOE'S REACH.

I KNOW YOU POLICEWOMEN CARRY GUNS. I WANT IT—UH—

WOULD YOU REPEAT THAT LAST REQUEST?

BLUB
BLUB
BLUB

THAT WAS ONE OF MY JUDO HOLDS. THERE ARE MORE.

I JUST DON'T PERMIT YOUNG MEN TO YANK MY SCARF AND SUBMERGE ME IN SALT BRINE. IS THAT CLEAR?

DIRTY COPPER!

I DON'T WANT TO HURT YOU, JOE, SO TELL ME WHEN YOU'VE HAD ENOUGH.

53

CARS 12 AND 4, SET UP ROADBLOCK AT INTERSECTION OF ROUTES 12 AND 22.

THAT'S WHY WE'RE STICKING TO THESE GRAVEL ROADS. I KNOW THEM BY HEART! WE'LL BE SAFE HERE.

BUT, FLATTOP, EVENTUALLY WE'VE GOT TO GO UP ON A HIGHWAY.

THINK SO? LOOK AT THIS MAP. I CAN TRAVEL THE ENTIRE LENGTH OF THIS STATE AND NEVER TOUCH A HIGHWAY. I USE UNDERPASSES.

I REPEAT, FLATTOP, YOU'RE ABSOLUTELY A GENIUS.

OH, COME NOW! TURN ON THE HI-FI SET, EH, JOE?

THIS MILD SPRING DAY A RURAL MAIL CARRIER RIDES HIS ROUTE, ENJOYING THE FIRST SPRING WARMTH, WHEN—

THIS I'VE GOT TO CHECK!

TOO SHINY FOR A PIECE OF TIN—LOOKS MORE LIKE A MIRROR.

A WOMAN'S PURSE?

THERE'S BEEN A NAME ON THE LINING, BUT IT IS PARTIALLY TORN OUT···"POLICE DEPARTMENT-CITY—PLAINCLOTHES DIVISION". H'M?

JASPER COUNTY SHERIFF'S OFFICE TO DICK TRACY—CAN YOU COME TO ALDEN TO VIEW SOME EVIDENCE?

WE'RE JUST GETTING READY TO BOARD A PLANE—WHAT KIND OF EVIDENCE?

A POLICE-WOMAN'S HANDBAG.

A POLICE-WOMAN'S HANDBAG?

SHERIFF, WHICH WAY IS ALDEN?

WANT A COLA?

DON'T CARE IF I DO.

FEEL BEHIND THAT REAR CUSHION TO YOUR RIGHT.

THEY'RE THE FINEST WIRE CUTTERS MADE. IN FACT, THEY'LL CUT A QUARTER-INCH BOLT.

BUT WHY, FLATTOP?

THE TWO ARE BELIEVED TO BE AVOIDING THE HIGHWAYS BY TRAVELING THE GRAVEL ROADS.

WE MAY HAVE TO GO THROUGH FENCES.

FLATTOP, HAVE YOU GOT ANY MORE SANDWICHES IN THAT REFRIGERATOR?

I'VE GOT BETTER THAN THAT. HERE ARE SOME EGGS.

EGGS?

PUSH THAT BUTTON ON THE BACK OF THE RIGHT FRONT SEAT.

OH, NO! A HOT PLATE—WITH A SKILLET!

58

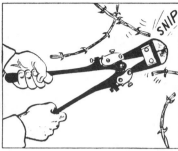

YES, THAT'S THE LAST OF IT. THAT MAKES THREE BAGS OF RED PAINT YOU'VE DROPPED ON 'EM.

OKAY— BOMBS AWAY.

THEY'RE MARKING THE CAR WITH RED PAINT SO IT CAN BE QUICKLY SPOTTED WHEN IT HITS THE HIGHWAY AGAIN.

WE CAN'T GO ON, FLATTOP. THAT LAST ONE COVERED THE WINDSHIELD. YOU CAN'T SEE.

THEY'RE STILL FOLLOWING KITTY CREEK, HEADED SOUTH—ABOUT A MILE NORTH OF DEVON.

2-WAY WRIST RADIO

THEY MAY BE PREPARING TO PULL UP ONTO DEVON AVENUE.

DON'T WORRY, TRACY, THREE SQUADS OF US ARE READY AND WAITING FOR THEM.

WAITING FOR US, ARE THEY? OKAY, WE'LL TURN AROUND.

THEY'VE REVERSED THEMSELVES— THEY'VE HEADED BACK NORTH.

WHAAT?

BUMP BUMP.

NOW WHAT, FLATTOP?

GET OUT, AND I'LL SHOW YOU.

THEY JUST DROVE THEIR CAR UNDER A SMALL BRIDGE AND STOPPED— THAT'S ALL.

WHAT'S THE ROAD, TRACY?

A FARM ROAD.

—RUNS EAST AND WEST CONNECTING TWO OTHER GRAVEL ROADS, THREE MILES NORTH OF ROUTE 62.

YOU'LL FIND NEWSPAPERS IN THE TRUNK, JOE. GET THEM OUT AND ROLL UP YOUR SLEEVES.

61

DO THEY THINK FOR ONE MINUTE THEY'VE LOST US, TRACY, JUST BECAUSE THEY DASHED UNDER A BRIDGE?

NO, BOB, THEY'RE NOT THAT DUMB! THEY'RE UP TO SOMETHING ELSE.

DO YOU WANT A WHOLE PAILFUL, FLATTOP?

YES, SEVERAL PAILFULS.

IT'LL TAKE THE SQUADS TEN MINUTES TO GET UP HERE FROM DEVON. WE'D BETTER JUST HOVER AND KEEP WATCH.

THE TERRAIN DROPS OFF QUITE SHARPLY ON THE OTHER SIDE OF THE BRIDGE, BOB.

MAYBE YOU CAN DESCEND LOW ENOUGH SO WE CAN SEE WHAT THE BOYS ARE DOING.

FANTASTIC LITTLE AIR CURRENTS IN THESE RAVINES—GOT TO WATCH.

AND WE DO HAVE TO KEEP MOBILE SO WE CAN FOLLOW THEM IF THEY TAKE OFF.

HEY, FLATTOP! THEY'RE GOING TO LAND!

IT ISN'T WORTH IT, TRACY! THESE QUARTERS ARE TOO CLOSE.

YOU'RE RIGHT, BOB. PULL UP TO 300 FEET LIKE WE WERE. WE'LL JUST STAND WATCH TILL THE SQUADS ARRIVE

BUT THOSE TRICKY AIR CURRENTS—AND THE NARROW CLEARANCE BETWEEN TREES—

CRACK

WHEN THE 'COPTER'S REVOLVING ROTOR BRUSHES A TREE LIMB—THERE'S A SNAP AND A MOMENT OF CRAZY SWAYING—AND **PLOP!**

ARE YOU ALL RIGHT TRACY?

YES.

—BUT WE MUSTN'T LOSE SIGHT OF THOSE KIDS UNDER THE BRIDGE.

THE SQUADS HAVE ARRIVED!

YEAH—BUT WHAT TH—

THEY'RE NOT HERE.

GONE! —CAR AND ALL, TRACY!

YOU'RE SURE THIS IS THE RIGHT BRIDGE, TRACY?

ARE YOU KIDDIN'? LOOK AT THESE FRESH TRACKS.

WHAT'S THIS STUFF?

WADS OF PAPER? WITH GOOEY STUFF—THAT'S PAINT AND DIRT!

62

DIRT WOULD MIX WITH THAT FRESH PAINT ENOUGH, SO THAT BY USING PIECES OF NEWSPAPER, THEY COULD WIPE THE CAR CLEAN.

DURING THE 4 OR 5 MINUTES ED AND I WERE SETTING DOWN THE DISABLED 'COPTER, THE BOYS MUST HAVE LAMMED.

ALL WE KNOW IS THEY ARE IN A YELLOW DEPONT SEDAN—BEARING AN OUT-OF-STATE LICENSE PLATE THAT NOBODY'S BEEN ABLE TO READ.

TRACKS SHOW THEY HEADED FOR THE SUPER-EXPRESSWAY. THAT MEANS THE CITY.

YES, TRACY, THE CITY! BUT TO TELL THE TRUTH, FLATTOP AND JOE PERIOD DIDN'T QUITE REACH THE CITY.

THE MAN SAID WE COULD STAY HERE AS LONG AS WE WANT, FOR A DOLLAR A DAY, JOE.

WE'RE AT THE MOST REMOTE PART OF THE TRAILER CAMP. WE WON'T BE SEEN BACK HERE.

DID YOU GET THE TURPENTINE AND CHEESECLOTH? YEAH. HOW ABOUT THE CHOW, JOE?

IF THOSE SMEARS DON'T COME COMPLETELY OFF, WE'D BETTER REPAINT THIS JOB. YEAH.

FLATTOP'S BOY! I CAN'T GET OVER IT! WHAT A LUCKY DAY WHEN WE MET! YEAH.

WE'LL GO THROUGH THICK AND THIN TOGETHER, EH, FLATTOP? NO MATTER WHAT HAPPENS! FRIENDS FOREVER! SHAKE, JOE.

AND AT "NOTHING" YONSON'S— I KEEP DREAMING HE'S ALIVE! I SEE HIM COME THROUGH THAT DOOR—HIS HANDS GO TO MY THROAT— BUT HE BLED TO DEATH RIGHT IN THIS ROOM! ARE YOU NUTS?

GOLDEN GATE TRAILER CAMP

DID YOU NOTICE THE CAR THAT CAME IN LAST NIGHT WITH THEM TWO KIDS IN IT? NO, WHY?

IT HAS A BUILT-IN TELEVISION—AND AN ELECTRIC STOVE! I SAW THEM FRYING EGGS A WHILE AGO. SO WHAT? YOU SEE ALL KINDS OF VEHICLES IN A TRAILER CAMP.

PAINT IN PRESSURIZED CANS! WE'RE GOING TO REPAINT THIS OLD CHARIOT.

64

THE BOYS APPARENTLY SMELLED A MOUSE AND TOOK OFF WITHOUT GOING BACK TO THE FILLING STATION FOR THEIR BATTERY.

THEY LEFT THESE MILK CARTONS AND RUBBISH IN THE TRAILER CAMP, ALONG WITH THAT PIECE OF CORRUGATED CARDBOARD WITH THE PENCILED SKETCH ON IT.

IT'S GOT TO BE YONSON'S RESTAURANT! THERE'S VESSEY STREET—AND THIRD.

WHAT'S YOUR INTERPRETATION OF THIS, TRACY?

"NOTHING" YONSON TRIED TO KILL JOE PERIOD, AND NOW JOE IS RETURNING TO THE CITY WITH JUST ONE OBJECT IN MIND—REVENGE ON "NOTHING" YONSON.

AND THAT'S WHERE WE'LL NAB BOTH JOE PERIOD AND HIS JERK PAL, FLATTOP.

YOU MEAN WE'RE GOING TO SIT ON YONSON'S PLACE TILL THOSE LITTLE MURDERERS SHOW UP?

WE'RE GOING TO DO IT THE EASY WAY, LIZZ, WITH OUR BATTERY-POWERED TELEVISION CAMERAS.

HOUSED IN THEIR CASES, THEY LOOK LIKE TERMINAL BOXES—ESPECIALLY AT A DISTANCE—HIGH ON A POLE.

BETTER GET OUR PUBLIC SERVICE PAL, FREDDY, AND HIS TRUCK.

WE'LL CHANNEL THEIR PIC INTO THESE MONITORS. A ENTERING OR LEAVING YO PLACE WILL BE SEEN

NOTE: SELF-CONTAINED ATOMIC POWER. NO ELECTRIC CABLES.

IT SEEMS TO ME THERE'S ONE LITTLE JOKER IN YOUR SCHEME, MR. TRACY. SUPPOSE THE KILLERS CATCH UP WITH YONSON SOME PLACE OTHER THAN AT HIS RESTAURANT—SAY AT HIS HOME OR IN THE PARK—OR ON THE STREET?

WHAT DO YOU MEAN? DIDN'T YOUR FRIEND, ANITA, THE PHOTOGRAPHER, TELL YOU YONSON WAS A NERVOUS WRECK THESE DAYS—AND NEVER LEFT HIS OFFICE?

YOU'RE RIGHT! SHE DID SAY THAT.

"BUT SOMEHOW, I JUST DON'T BELIEVE IT," SAYS LIZZ. "NOTHING' YONSON WAS ALWAYS A FEARLESS TYPE. HE NEVER LET ANYTHING SCARE HIM, AS LONG AS HE WAS ARMED."

NOTHING, LET ME IN.

BUT IT'S ONLY ME, JERRY THE WAITER, WITH YOUR SUPPER.

YEAH? SET IT DOWN OUTSIDE THE DOOR. I'LL GET IT LATER.

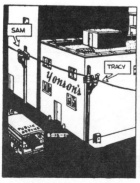

YONSON'S

SAM

TRACY

PUBLIC SERVICE

HOW'S THAT, CHIEF? IS THE ANGLE OKAY?

2-WAY WRIST RADIO

VERY GOOD! —PICTURES ARE NICE AND CLEAR.

WE HAVE TWO CAMERAS TRAINED ON THE FRONT ENTRANCE AND TWO ON THE BACK. OKAY?

PERFECT!

68

IT'S FOUR A.M., TRACY. THE GARBAGE MAN JUST LEFT THE RESTAURANT. THE PLACE IS CLOSED UP TIGHT.

NO SIGN OF THE BOYS?

NOT A SIGN. THE LAST TO LEAVE WERE THE ENTERTAINERS AND WAITERS.

WHAT ABOUT THE FRONT DOOR?

JUST THE ORDINARY RUN OF CUSTOMERS. NO KIDS ENTERED OR LEFT.

I'LL TAKE IT TILL NINE O'CLOCK, SAM, WHILE YOU GET YOURSELF SOME SHUTEYE.

MAYBE MY HUNCH WAS WRONG. MAYBE JOE PERIOD WON'T RETURN TO YONSON'S.

AND IN 'NOTHING' YONSON'S STRONGHOLD

THERE IT GOES AGAIN— I HEARD IT!

HONEST, "NOTHING," WE DIDN'T HEAR ANYTHING EXCEPT THAT ICE BOX COMPRESSOR POUNDING. THERE'S NOBODY AROUND.

THIS IS MORE OF A SCRAPING NOISE— I THINK—

HE'S REALLY GOING NUTS. I NEVER SAW A GUY CRACK UP SO FAST.

AND HE ALWAYS HAD NERVES OF STEEL.

THEY'RE RIGHT! FOUR WALLS AROUND ME—THREE CHAIN LOCKS ON MY DOOR AND GUARDS IN THE HALL. NO ONE CAN GET AT ME.

SURE, ICE BOX COMPRESSOR! BUCKY'S RIGHT! I'VE HEARD IT A THOUSAND TIMES—OLD FAMILIAR SOUNDS— ZZZZZZZ

THERE! THAT OUGHT TO DO IT.

NOW, PULL, FLATTOP, PULL.

CRUNCH

ODOR OF LIQUOR—AND HE SEEMS TO BE IN A DEEP SLEEP.

69

LOOK OUT—THAT'S A TOMMY GUN!

GOT IT!

THIS IS IT—BOYS! YOU'RE THROUGH!

I KNEW HE COULDN'T FIRE THIS. THE ACTUATOR WAS IN FORWARD POSITION, MAKING IT IMPOSSIBLE TO SHOOT. HE FORGOT TO PULL IT BACK!

HEY—THERE'S ANOTHER!

PUT 'EM UP, JOE— THIS IS FOR REAL!

IMAGINE! WATCHING A GANG CAPTURE BY TELEVISION!

THERE'S STILL ONE MORE—WHERE'S FLATTOP'S BOY?

HANDCUFF THEM THROUGH THEIR BELTS—HANDS BEHIND BACK.

LET'S GO INSIDE.

THEY BORED THEIR WAY UP THROUGH THE FLOOR FROM THE WINE CELLAR.

SAFE'S CLEANED OUT!

THE REASON THE BOYS WEREN'T SEEN ENTERING THE PLACE, ON THE TV, IS THEY USED A SMALL WINDOW IN THIS NARROW AREAWAY BETWEEN THE BUILDINGS.

THE WINDOW HAD BEEN SEALED UP YEARS AGO—BUT THEY CUT RIGHT THROUGH THE PANELING.

YOU SAY JOE DID IT? ARE YOU WILLING TO SIGN A DYING STATEMENT TO THAT EFFECT?

YES---JOE PERIOD SHOT ME—I'LL SIGN--- I'LL SIGN---

WHERE'S FLATTOP?

HE IS BELIEVED HEADED NORTH ON ROUTE 3. A DESCRIPTION OF CAR AS FOLLOWS---

CHESTER GOULD

THERE'S HIS STATEMENT. WE GOT HIS SIGNATURE ON IT JUST BEFORE HE DIED.

YOU HEARD "NOTHING" YONSON'S STATEMENT, JOE. YOU'VE GOT A MURDER CHARGE ON YOUR HANDS.

AND ELSEWHERE

THE LITTLE BOX HAS OVER TEN GRAND IN IT.

CHESTER GOULD

NOW TO MIX THE COMBINATION AND RELAX! I'M RICH!

YES, FLATTOP'S CAR NOT ONLY HAS A HI-FI SET, A REFRIGERATOR, A TV RE- CEIVER, A SINK WITH RUNNING WATER, A STOVE, AIR CONDITIONING, A SHORT- WAVE SET, BUT IT ALSO HAS A COMBINATION SAFE!

THE FUTILITY OF A LIFE OF CRIME MUST BE PRETTY OBVIOUS TO YOU BY NOW, JOE.

YOU MURDERED YOUR FORMER HERO, "NOTHING" YONSON, AND YOU YOURSELF ARE HEADED FOR THE ELECTRIC CHAIR.

WHO SAYS SO?

WHAT'S THIS?

STUCK IN LOOPS INSIDE HIS PANTS BAND.

ONE OF THOSE PEN GUNS?

NO. A STEEL PICK!

HEY! THIS IS WHAT WE'VE BEEN WAITING FOR.

AND UNDER HIS BELT! A STEEL PICK—A VICIOUS THING—

POCKETCLIP? THE GUY WHO DIED IN THAT HOTEL CORRIDOR? YES—SURE... THE AUTOPSY SHOWED IT. ---YES.

THE CORONER'S COMING OVER, SAM, WITH THE AUTOPSY REPORT AND THE EVIDENCE.

YOU MEAN THIS KILLED POCKETCLIP?

AND BACK TO FLATTOP— YES, I'M RICH NOW—I CAN AFFORD A STEAK!

WHEN I GET TO THE CITY, I'LL RENT A GARAGE FOR MY CAR AND LIVE RIGHT IN THE CAR.

I CAN COOK, WATCH TV, SLEEP AND EAT—JUST LIKE IN A ROOM! WHAT A HIDE-OUT IT'LL BE!

AND THAT STEEL SAFE WITH THE TEN GRAND IN IT WILL ASSURE ME PERMANENT WHEREWITHAL!

MEANWHILE

JOE, YOUR MOTHER'S IN THE VISITORS' ROOM.

MY MOTHER? @X!!*~*!

JOE!

A FINE TIME TO COME AND SEE ME!

A FINE MOTHER YOU ARE! WHERE HAVE YOU BEEN THE LAST THREE YEARS?

IS IT TRUE, SON? IS IT TRUE?

WHY SHOULD I TALK TO YOU? TAKE HER AWAY!

YEAH. WANT TO TAKE A LOOK, LIZZ?

SO THAT'S HOW PAUL POCKETCLIP DIED?

MURPHY, ASK THE CHIEF TO COME IN—HE WON'T BELIEVE THIS!

I'M ABSOLUTELY FLABBERGASTED.

AND IN THE VISITORS' ROOM—

NO, SON, I'M THE DELINQUENT ONE —NOT YOU—I'M THE ONE.

OKAY— YOU'VE SAID IT. NOW—GO! GO!

YEAH, I DID ALL THREE OF 'EM, MA, JUST LIKE THE PAPER SAYS. THEY'VE GOT THE GOODS ON ME. I THOUGHT I WAS SMART, BUT I WAS DUMB.

AS YOUR MOTHER, I MADE MY MISTAKE 15 YEARS AGO! I INSISTED ON WORKING IN THE FACTORY ALONGSIDE YOUR DAD, WHEN I SHOULD HAVE BEEN HOME CARING FOR YOU.

YOUR DAD AND I WENT OUT EVERY NIGHT—NIGHTS WHEN YOU NEEDED US. WE NEGLECTED OUR CHURCH TO CAROUSE. WE LAUGHED AT YOUR FIRST BRUSH WITH THE LAW—THOUGHT IT WAS FUNNY---

WE FORGOT THERE WAS SUCH A WORD AS "PUNISH" IN THIS GREAT SCHEME OF THINGS---WE WERE "MODERN"---WE WERE FOOLS! THEN, AFTER YOUR DAD DIED IN THE CAR CRASH—IT WAS TOO LATE. YOU WERE GROWN UP THEN.

GET HER OUT OF HERE BEFORE I RUN MY FIST THROUGH THIS GLASS—

JUVENILE PROBLEM? WHAT ABOUT THE PARENT PROBLEM? PARENTS LIKE ME!

YES, CHIEF, JOE PERIOD HAD THIS ON HIM WHEN WE PINCHED HIM—IT TELLS A LOT.

A STEEL PICK?

REMEMBER POCKETCLIP, THE LOVESICK PLAYBOY WHO DIED IN A HOTEL CORRIDOR WHILE CALLING ON LIZZ'S SISTER, THE SINGER?

SURE, AT FIRST IT WAS THOUGHT HE HAD A HEART ATTACK.

HOWEVER, AUTOPSY SHOWED HE DIED FROM A NEARLY INVISIBLE WOUND AT THE BASE OF THE SKULL.

AND THIS TINY BIT OF METAL WAS RECOVERED

NOW, LOOK AT THAT WEAPON AND THE LITTLE PIECE OF METAL UNDER THE STERBOSCOPE.

CHIEF, THIS ONE BIT OF EVIDENCE ALONE WILL SEND JOE PERIOD TO THE ELECTRIC CHAIR.

STEEL PICK FOUND ON JOE PERIOD

RECOVERED FROM VICTIM

"THE SAD PART OF THIS CASE IS—THERE'S STILL ANOTHER WHO'S HEADED IN THE SAME DIRECTION," SAYS TRACY. "I THINK I KNOW WHO YOU MEAN," REPLIES THE CHIEF.

CHESTER GOULD

STEEL PICK FOUND ON JOE PERIOD

RECOVERED FROM VICTIM

ALL RIGHT—SO I'M HEADED FOR THE CHAIR—OKAY. JUST KEEP HER OUT OF HERE—THAT'S ALL I ASK.

SHE NEVER WORRIED ABOUT ME BEFORE. WHY DOES SHE COME SOBBING AROUND HERE NOW?

JOE, I'M YOUR MOTHER.

I KNOW I FAILED! I FAILED TO DEVOTE MYSELF TO MY BOY! CAN YOU FORGIVE ME, JOE? CAN YOU FORGIVE ME?

BEAT IT!

CHESTER GOULD

SHE LEAPED RIGHT IN FRONT OF THE TRUCK!

THE DRIVER DIDN'T HAVE A CHANCE. I SAW IT ALL.

DEAD?

WHAT DO YOU THINK? IT WAS A TEN-TON TRAILER JOB.

—ALL I KNOW IS, THEY'VE GOT SOMETHING TO TELL YOU ABOUT YOUR MOTHER.

UP ONE ALLEY AND DOWN ANOTHER—FLATTOP LOOKS FOR A PRIVATE GARAGE WITH A VACANCY SIGN—

FOR RENT
Inquire rear apartment

THE GARAGE WILL BE $10 A MONTH —IN ADVANCE.

THERE'S YOUR TEN.

AND HERE'S THE KEY. YOU'LL FIND A PADLOCK ON THE ALLEY DOOR.

WHAT COULD BE SWEETER? I'LL SLEEP RIGHT HERE TONIGHT—AND TOMORROW, MAYBE I'LL LOOK FOR A ROOM.

LOOKING FOR SOMEONE?

LOOKING FOR A ROOM. I SAW THE SIGN IN FRONT.

AN ART STUDENT? —YOU'D BETTER SPEAK TO MY MOTHER.

CAN YOU PAY? I'M NOT RUNNING A CHARITY HOUSE HERE! YOU YOUNG PEOPLE ARE ALWAYS BROKE.

I CAN PAY.

FOLLOW ME.

TRACY, DIET SMITH JUST DROPPED IN WITH SOME NEW MODELS OF THE 2-WAY WRIST RADIO.

DO YOU REALIZE, SAM, YOU'VE BEEN USING THE 2-WAY WRIST RADIO SINCE JANUARY, 1946?

OVER TEN YEARS?

ITS ATOM BATTERY POWER IS EXACTLY THE SAME AS IN 1946, BUT AN IMPROVED CIRCUIT GIVES IT A 2-WAY RANGE OF OVER 2500 MILES, INSTEAD OF THE ORIGINAL 500.

CA1713X— CAN YOU HEAR ME?

COMING IN VERY CLEAR.

THAT'S HIS EXPERIMENTAL RESEARCH STATION IN IOWA.

HIEF, DO YOU REALIZE THAT YOUR DEPARTMENT HAS BEEN USING THE 2-WAY WRIST RADIO IN THE APPREHENSION OF CRIMINALS FOR OVER 10 YEARS?

TEN YEARS?

YES, CHIEF, DIET SMITH'S LAB PERFECTED AND TURNED OVER TO US THE FIRST 2-WAY WRIST RADIO IN JANUARY, 1946.

THERE STILL IS NO 2-WAY WRIST RADIO LIKE IT ANYWHERE IN THE WORLD. IT'S UNIQUE. IT'S COMPLETELY SELF-CONTAINED, AND HAS A SENDING AND RECEIVING RANGE OF OVER 2500 MILES!

THE ATOM BATTERY THAT FURNISHES THE POWER IS STRICTLY A DIET SMITH SECRET.

OTHERS HAVE COME UP WITH WRIST RADIOS—YES, YOU'LL SEE SOME AT THE CONVENTIONS...

SPEAKER   ATOM

BUT THEY'RE NOT LIKE OURS—THEY HAVE EARPLUGS, WIRES, AERIALS--- WHOOIE!

SPEAKING OF THE NEWEST, DIET SMITH'S BATTERY-POWERED TV CAMERAS WERE THE PRIME REASON WE WERE ABLE TO CAPTURE JOE PERIOD.

SCIENCE IS GREAT, BOYS —WE ALL KNOW THAT— BUT WHAT ABOUT THIS LAD, FLATTOP?

WHAT HAVE YOU TO REPORT ON HIM?

CHIEF, I UNDERSTAND THIS BOY FLATTOP IS AN ELECTRICAL GENIUS! —HAS HIS CAR EQUIPPED WITH AN ELECTRIC STOVE—A TV SET— A REFRIGERATOR.

YES, SO WHAT?

JUST THIS, CHIEF—NEXT WEEK MY COMPANY IS GOING TO RUN BIG ADS IN ALL THE NEWS-PAPERS. WE WANT TO HIRE YOUNG ELECTRONICS STUDENTS. MAYBE FLATTOP WILL BE AMONG THE APPLICANTS.

AH, NUTS! NOT THAT LITTLE CROOK.

MEANWHILE, FLATTOP'S CAR RESTS SAFELY BEHIND THE DOORS OF A RENTED GARAGE.

AND FLATTOP HIMSELF, POSING AS AN ART STUDENT—HAS TAKEN QUARTERS IN A CHEAP ROOMING HOUSE.

AND THE RENT WILL BE TEN DOLLARS A WEEK IN ADVANCE.

SO YOU'RE AN ART STUDENT, MR. JONES? WELL, WELCOME TO OUR HOUSE! MANY YOUNG GENIUSES HAVE STARTED OUT FROM THIS ROOM.

WHAT MEDIUM DO YOU WORK IN?

SLAM

WELL!! ALL I ASKED HIM WAS, "WHAT MEDIUM DO YOU WORK IN?" THAT'S ALL.

MOTHER, YOU'RE SO NOSY! YOU KNOW ARTISTS LIKE PRIVACY.

BUT I DIDN'T MEAN ANY HARM.

I LOOK UPON ALL MY ROOMERS AS MY CHILDREN —I—I TRY TO BE A MOTHER TO THEM.

I WANT THEM TO KNOW I'M INTERESTED IN THEM—THAT THEIR TROUBLES ARE MY TROUBLES—OH BOO-HOO —HOO-HOO—

GOSH, I HOPE YOU WON'T THINK I'M NOSY, BUT NEITHER MOTHER NOR I ASKED YOU YOUR FIRST NAME.

JUST JONES.

OH, MR. JONES, I HOPE YOU WON'T MIND MOTHER. SHE'S SUCH A DEAR—AND SHE TRIES SO HARD TO MAKE EVERYONE FEEL AT HOME.

SKINNY! STOP YAPPING WITH THAT NEW JERK AND GET DOWN HERE **AND HELP WITH THESE DIRTY DISHES!**

YES, MOTHER.

BOW WOW WOW

CAR 41-10-207--- 10-4 GO TO 1832 SOUTH PARK, ROBBERY IN PROGRESS--- 10-4---

SIC 'EM, BEENY! SIC 'EM! GO AHEAD.

ER—HELLO, MR. JONES! ER—YOU COMFORTABLE? ALL OKAY? EVERYTHING ALL RIGHT?

MOTHER! WHAT ARE YOU DOING?

I JUST DON'T LIKE HIS ATTITUDE, THAT'S ALL.

FLATTOP'S TRAIL HAS GROWN COMPLETELY COLD, SO TRACY, SAM AND LIZZ HAVE DRIVEN BACK TO SEE FLATTOP'S AUNT AGAIN.

WE HAVEN'T FOUND THE BOY AND WE THOUGHT WE'D BETTER TALK TO YOU AGAIN.

COME IN, PLEASE.

GO AHEAD, MR. JONES. BEENY AND I WILL MODEL FOR YOU. GO AHEAD.

OH, IT'S QUITE ALL RIGHT—I'M A PROFESSIONAL MODEL. I ENJOY IT.

BUT I'M NOT HIRING A MODEL. I DON'T EVEN PAINT PORTRAITS.

MR. JONES, THIS IS FOR FREE. I OFTEN SIT FOR DIFFERENT STUDENTS— GRATIS.

BUT I'M A LANDSCAPE MAN MYSELF—ALWAYS HAVE BEEN.

WHY DON'T YOU TRY FIGURE WORK JUST ONCE? _ALL_ GOOD ARTISTS SKETCH FROM LIVE MODELS.

WELL —OKAY.

BEING HIS AUNT, IT WAS NATURAL THAT I SHOULD RAISE FLATTOP AFTER HIS FATHER DIED.

I WAS A WIDOW—AND HAD TO WORK DAYS. EVEN AS A LITTLE BOY, HE WOULD STEAL COINS FROM THE SUGAR BOWL.

BUT I EXCUSED IT BECAUSE HE USED THE MONEY TO BUY ELECTRONIC PARTS. HE BUILT A RADIO THAT WORKED, WHEN HE WAS ONLY 8 YEARS OLD.

AW— THIS IS LOUSY!

NOW, MR. JONES, DON'T SAY THAT— YOU'RE GOOD!

76

HE WAS IN HERE NOT MORE THAN 2 DAYS AGO AND BOUGHT SEVERAL TUBES OF COLOR. WHAT ABOUT HIM?

SEE THAT SIGNATURE? WE JUST WANT HIM, THAT'S ALL.

IF HE COMES IN AGAIN, HOLD HIM IN CONVERSATION AND HAVE SOMEONE GIVE US A RING.

FLATTOPS BOY? HOLY NED! BUT DON'T WORRY ABOUT ME, MR. TRACY, I KEEP A LOADED 30-30 BACK OF THAT PARTITION.

LISTEN, MY FRIEND, FORGET YOUR 30-30! JUST PHONE US IF HE COMES IN. THIS IS A JOB FOR THE POLICE. THAT MAN IS WANTED FOR MURDER AND ASSAULT TO KILL.

HEY, I JUST HAPPENED TO THINK—I WON'T BE HERE TOMORROW. I'M ONE OF THE JUDGES AT THE ART SHOW.

THE ART SHOW?

AND AT THE ROOMING HOUSE—

YOU'RE PURE GENIUS— JUST PURE GENIUS!

UGH—TAKE THAT COLD CHICKEN AWAY— IT'S MAKING ME SICK—UGH!

OH, JONESY, I CAN'T HOLD IT ANY LONGER! I-I'VE GOT GREAT NEWS FOR YOU—I MUST TELL YOU!

I ENTERED ONE OF YOUR PAINTINGS IN THE CIVIC CENTER ART SHOW—I TOOK IT THERE WHILE YOU WERE ASLEEP ---YOU'LL BE FAMOUS---I JUST KNOW YOU WILL!

SKINNY! GET DOWN HERE AND HELP WITH THESE DIRTY DISHES! SKINNY!

SKINNY! GET DOWN HERE! Y'HEAR ME?

OH, MY JAW! HE-HE STRUCK ME! HE HIT ME WITH HIS FIST!

JUST WHAT HAS TRANSPIRED BETWEEN YOU AND THAT FLAT-HEADED MORON NOW?

DID HE GO OUT, MOTHER?

GOT TO GET IT BACK! THIS COULD LEAD TO BIG TROUBLE.

GOT TO GET THAT PAINTING, BUT I CAN'T SEE IT—

MR. EVERS, WOULD YOU GET THE OTHER JUDGE, PLEASE?

SO THERE IT IS!—BEHIND ALL THOSE PEOPLE. I'LL SNATCH IT AS SOON AS THEY MOVE.

HAVE YOU THE BLUE RIBBON, MRS. PINKLE?

YES, HERE IT IS.

BETTER HAVE A GUARD STATIONED HERE. THIS IS A VALUABLE PAINTING NOW.

NO CHANCE TO SNATCH IT— WITH THAT GANG OF YOKELS AROUND IT—BUT WHY? WHY ARE THEY THERE?

FLATTOP DOESN'T KNOW IT— BUT AT THIS SAME MOMENT SKINNY, THE MODEL IS GETTING A PHONE CALL.

FIRST PRIZE?

YES, AND WON'T YOU COME RIGHT DOWN? THE MAYOR IS WAITING TO PRESENT YOU THE CHECK BEFORE ALL THE NEWS-PAPER AND TV CAMERAMEN.

JUST ANOTHER ONE, PLEASE.

IS THIS YOUR FIRST WIN IN ART COMPETITION, MISS SKINNER?

WHERE DID YOU STUDY, MISS SKINNER?

UH-HUH. UH-HUH.

THE "YESTERDAY" SHOW WOULD LIKE YOU FOR AN INTERVIEW, MISS SKINNER.

WOULD YOU LIKE TO APPEAR ON "FRAMEUP", MISS SKINNER?

PEAS

FLATTOP'S PAINTING TAKES FIRST PRIZE—AND SKINNY, THE MODEL, TAKES THE CHECK—

I ENTERED THE PAINTING UNDER MY NAME, AND EVERYBODY THINKS I'M THE ARTIST. I'M FAMOUS!

$500

BUT, SKINNY, YOU CAN'T KEEP THIS— YOU---CAN'T---

I CAN'T?

WHAT'S WORRYING YOU, MICHEL-ANGELO?

OH, BROTHER, THIS MODERN ART! YOU SHOULD SEE WHAT WON FIRST PRIZE.

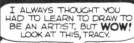

I ALWAYS THOUGHT YOU HAD TO LEARN TO DRAW TO BE AN ARTIST, BUT WOW! LOOK AT THIS, TRACY.

I'M NO ART CRITIC, KID. THE CHIEF SAID SO, HIMSELF. ANYWAY, MAYBE YOU'RE JUST OLD-FASHIONED.

SEEMS TO BE SOMETHING FAMILIAR—ABOUT IT.

TARGET RANGE

HEY, LIZZ!

THERE'S YOUR DOG! NOW, STAY OUT!

SKINNY, YOU'RE WANTED ON THE PHONE.

I'M MRS. JOHNSON, AND I'VE BEEN ADMIRING YOUR PRIZE-WINNING PAINTING AT THE ART SHOW.

Y-YES?

WE'RE BUILDING A NEW HOME, AND I WAS WONDERING IF YOU'D DO A COUPLE OF PAINTINGS FOR ME? MAY I COME OVER?

ER- HUH?

—AND I WAS WONDERING IF YOU'D DO A COUPLE OF PAINTINGS FOR ME—FOR MY NEW HOME— AT YOUR OWN PRICE, OF COURSE.

A LADY SAW THE PRIZE PAINTING, AND SHE WANTS TO COME OVER—

DON'T TURN TO ME! YOU GOT YOURSELF INTO THIS MESS!

H'M?

CERTAINLY, MRS. JOHNSON, COME RIGHT OVER—

ARE YOU CRAZY?

SO GLAD TO KNOW YOU, MISS SKINNER. I THINK YOU PAINT BEAUTIFULLY

THANK YOU.

MY STUDIO'S UPSTAIRS. WON'T YOU COME UP?

HUH? WHY, IT'S THAT POLICEWOMAN THAT JOE PERIOD AND I TRIED TO DROWN.

AND THEY'RE COMING UP HERE!

WHAT A CHARMING STUDIO!

THANK YOU.

WHAT IS SKINNY'S GAME?

OUR LIVING ROOM IS TO BE OF STONE AND WOOD, AND I'D LIKE TWO LANDSCAPES FOR THE FIREPLACE WALL.

PERHAPS YOU'D LIKE TO SEE MORE OF MY WORK.

AND FLATTOP, RECOGNIZING THE POLICEWOMAN, CRINGES IN THE CLOSET AS HE TRIES TO FIGURE OUT SKINNY'S GAME.

HOW ABOUT DOING TWO ESPECIALLY FOR ME, AT, SAY $500 APIECE?

$500?

THEN, YOU'LL DO TWO PAINTINGS FOR ME FOR $1,000?

YES, MA'AM.

THANKS, MRS. JOHNSON. I'LL CALL YOU WHEN THEY'RE READY

YOU DIRTY LITTLE RAT! WHAT'S YOUR GAME?

D'YA WANT TO KNOW?

HOW WOULD YOU LIKE TO WORK FOR ME?

WHAT HAPPENED?

KEEP BACK!

AND SHE WAS SUCH A BEAUTIFUL THING.

HER MOTHER TOLD MY MOTHER SHE WAS BOY-CRAZY.

FROM THAT ROOF REPAIR JOB ACROSS THE STREET, I SAW THE STRUGGLE. HE HURLED HER TO THE STREET. THEN HE RAN TO THIS GARAGE AND DROVE AWAY.

I SAW THE SCUFFLING, THEN SUDDENLY HE PICKED HER UP AND HELD HER OVER HIS HEAD.

WE FOUND ONE OF HER SHOES AND A PAIR OF GLASSES UP HERE, TRACY.

LATER, AT THE MORGUE, THAT GRIM ROUTINE WHICH FOLLOWS EVERY MURDER PROCEEDS SILENTLY—

EXAMINATION OF THE VICTIM'S HAND CLUTCHING A FEW HAIRS

THEN CLOSE INSPECTION OF THE FINGERS AND NAILS FOR PARTICLES WHICH MAY CONTRIBUTE TO A DESCRIPTION OF THE MURDERER.

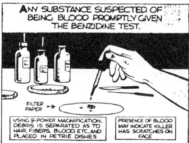

ANY SUBSTANCE SUSPECTED OF BEING BLOOD PROMPTLY GIVEN THE BENZIDINE TEST.

FILTER PAPER

USING 9-POWER MAGNIFICATION, DEBRIS IS SEPARATED AS TO HAIR, FIBERS, BLOOD, ETC. AND PLACED IN PETRIE DISHES

PRESENCE OF BLOOD MAY INDICATE KILLER HAS SCRATCHES ON FACE

THE EVIDENCE THEN FOLDED INTO CLEAN PAPER AND LABELED.

AND THE RECORDS ARE FILED.—RECORDS THAT TELL A STORY AS VIVIDLY AS A CAMERA SHOT! AND "SKINNY" THE MODEL IS JUST ANOTHER CASE.

THE FLIGHT—

WH—WHO—? ??!

DID SOMETHING BRUSH AGAINST MY CHEEK? MAYBE A BUG? OR A PIECE OF PAPER FROM THE FLOOR???

AY — GET AWAY! HUH? NO, IT'S MY IMAGINATION! THERE'S NO ONE IN THIS CAR BUT ME.

I SAW HER FALL—SHE CAN'T BOTHER ME ANY MORE. I'M OKAY—JUST GOT TO GET HOLD OF MYSELF.

SHOES AND GLASSES FROM THE ROOF! FINGERNAIL SCRAPINGS THAT PROVE A STRUGGLE TOOK PLACE!

YES, SAM, IT'S AN AIRTIGHT CASE OF MURDER.

CAR 10 REPORTS SIGHTING FLATTOP'S CAR AND IS NOW PURSUING HIM DOWN BELMONT AVENUE.

THEY'RE TOO CLOSE FOR COMFORT! GOT TO SLOW 'EM UP—

?

YES, A **SMOKE SCREEN!** I TELL YOU—THE GUY PRODUCED A SMOKE SCREEN THROUGH HIS EXHAUST.

I'D BETTER PULL INTO ONE OF THESE CONGESTED MARKET PARKING LOTS WHERE THERE'S SAFETY IN NUMBERS —

FOOD SUPER MART

—TILL I FIGURE OUT WHAT TO DO.

AWK!

IS THERE SOMETHING HANGING ON MY NECK, KID?

I DON'T SEE NOTHIN'. ARE YOU GOOFY?

FLATTOP WILL BE SO EASILY RECOGNIZED, IT'S TEN TO ONE HE'LL RESORT TO A DISGUISE OF SOME KIND.

I WANT YOU TO PREPARE SKETCHES, JUNIOR, SHOWING HIM WEARING A MUSTACHE, GLASSES, CREW-CUT, ETC.— TO BE PUT INTO A FLIER FOR CITY-WIDE DISTRIBUTION.

GEE, FLATTOP WITH A **CREW-CUT!** I BET THAT ALONE WOULD CHANGE HIS LOOKS.

GET AWAY---LET LOOSE--- **AWA!** TAKE YOUR HANDS OFF! UGH—

DRIVING DOWN BACK ALLEYS AND SIDE ROADS ALL NIGHT! IT'S JUST LUCK THE COPS HAVEN'T SPOTTED ME.

THERE GOES A SQUAD CAR, AND THEY'RE TURNING AROUND THE BLOCK! THEY SAW ME.

DRUGS

SITE OF CIVIC AUDITORIUM

A NAILED-UP OLD FIRETRAP ---BUT IT'LL HIDE ME! THEY CAN HAVE THE CAR.

MY NECK---I'M CHOKING---

BREAKING HIS WAY INTO AN ABANDONED BUILDING, FLATTOP WAITS FOR THE RETURN OF THE SQUAD CAR.

BUT IT DOESN'T RETURN! THEY DIDN'T SEE HIM AFTER ALL!

SHOULD HE CONTINUE THE LOSING GAME OF CRUISING THE CITY STREETS? OR SHOULD HE DASH FOR THE OPEN COUNTRYSIDE?

HE LOOKS ABOUT HIM, AS IF FOR AN ANSWER.

WHAT?

88

FLATTOP KNOWS HE'S SO HOT HE CAN'T SHOW HIS FACE—UNLESS HE RESORTS TO A DISGUISE.

JUNIOR HAS PREPARED SOME SKETCHES SHOWING HOW FLATTOP WOULD LOOK IN VARIOUS GETUPS.

GLASSES. MUSTACHE. CREW CUT. HAT. COMBINATION.

THE NEWSPAPERS WILL BE GLAD TO PRINT THESE. AND WE'LL HAVE FLIERS MADE FOR THE DIFFERENT DISTRICTS AND THE SHERIFF'S OFFICE. GREAT STUFF, KID.

MEANWHILE, THE PANICKY FLATTOP, HAVING FORCED HIS WAY INTO AN ABANDONED BUILDING, MAKES A DISCOVERY. A THEATER!

MUSTY, VERMIN-RIDDEN AND SILENT, THE RUINS SEEM TO ECHO HIS VERY HEART BEAT.

DOORS—THAT WERE USED TO BRING IN SCENERY. I WONDER IF THEY STILL—

THE BOLTS ARE RUSTY—BUT THEY GIVE UNDER FLATTOP'S TUGGING. CRUNCH

COMING SOON

AND THE OLD THEATER COMES TO LIFE AGAIN, IN A NEW DRAMA OF A CAR AND A MAN AND HIS CONSCIENCE.

WITH THE PASSING OF IMMEDIATE DANGER, FLATTOP OPENS THE SQUEAKY STAGE DOORS AND DRIVES HIS CAR INSIDE, WHERE HE NOW GLOATS OVER HIS CLEVERNESS. NOT BAD!

I'D BETTER PUT THE OLD BEAM BACK—JUST FOR SAFETY.

AND THE WINDOW I BROKE TO ENTER—I'LL BAR IT.

I'M ABSOLUTELY HID! THERE ISN'T A CHANCE IN THE WORLD THEY CAN FIND ME NOW.

89

INSTRUCTOR BARNECK WAS JUST SHOWING ME A JUDO TRICK THAT CAN BE USED IN DEFENSE AGAINST 2 ASSAILANTS AT THE SAME TIME.

LET'S SEE IT, LIZZ.

THIS TRICK SHOULD BE PRACTICED ONLY UNDER PROFESSIONAL SUPERVISION. OKAY—SWING AT HER, TRACY.

A KICK AT THE KNEE OF ONE ASSAILANT, AT THE SAME TIME SENDING HER ELBOWS TO THE SOLAR PLEXUSES OF BOTH MEN.

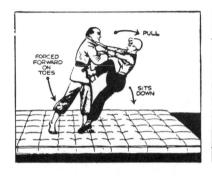

PULL

FORCED FORWARD ON TOES

SITS DOWN

THAT'S THE WAY. I'M GOING TO HANDLE FLATTOP WHEN WE MEET.

IN THIS CASE, I'M GLAD IT WAS INSTRUCTOR BARNECK INSTEAD OF ME. HE KNOWS HOW TO TAKE THOSE FALLS.

SPEAKING OF FLATTOP, LET US RETURN TO THE RAT-INFESTED RUINS OF THE OLD THEATER, WHERE FRUSTRATION AND GLOOM SET THE STAGE FOR ACT TWO—

AND NOW, RAIN! RIGHT THROUGH THE ROOF!

GOT TO KEEP THE WINDOWS ROLLED UP OR THEY'D TAKE THE FOOD RIGHT OUT OF MY MOUTH.

COPS OR NO COPS, I'M PULLING OUT OF THIS RATHOLE TONIGHT.

WHAT'S THAT NOISE?

NO, NO! A BUILDING PROJECT NEXT DOOR?

GRAVEL, SAND, BRICKS—RIGHT ACROSS THE BIG EXIT DOORS! I CAN'T GET MY CAR OUT!

I'M STUCK!

#3

CHESTER GOULD

YEAH, I'M STUCK! I CAN'T DRIVE MY CAR OUT! I'M SEALED IN!

THE CITY'S CLOSED THE ALLEY TO TRAFFIC. WE CAN STACK EVERYTHING AGAINST THE OLD THEATER WALL.

CHESTER GOULD

BUT I'M LOW ON FOOD. NO BREAD! HARDLY ANY MILK—NO EGGS!

THERE'S A SUPER-MARKET ON THE NEXT CORNER. BUT IF I SNEAKED OUT—EVEN AFTER DARK—I'D BE RECOGNIZED WITH THIS FLAT HEAD OF MINE.

THE CHECK-OUT GIRL AT THE SUPER-MARKET SPOTTED HIM WHEN HE WENT AFTER FOOD. THE BOYS ARE ON THE SCENE.

ALL THE EXITS ARE COVERED— WE'RE ALL SET.

OKAY— I'M GOING INSIDE.

IT'S NOT TOO LIGHT IN HERE, SAM. BETTER TIE HANDKERCHIEFS AROUND OUR HATS TO IDENTIFY US, IN CASE THERE'S A GUN BATTLE.

CAUTIOUS, TRACY! THERE'S A THOUSAND PLACES HE CAN HIDE.

WHAT? **THE ROOF!** WE FORGOT THE ROOF.

HEY, TRACY, HE'S **DOWN HERE!**

STICK 'EM UP, FLATTOP!

WITH SAM FIRING AT HIM, FLATTOP LEAPS FROM THE STAGE AND HEADS FOR THE LOBBY OF THE THEATER ON ALL FOURS.

I'LL CRASH MY WAY OUT—

THIS PLACE WILL BURN LIKE AN ORANGE CRATE!

HEY, TRACY!

THAT ROOF HATCH IS SPOUTING SOLID FLAME!

WHAT CAN HE DO?

CHESTER GOULD

HE SET SOME OLD DRAPES AFIRE! THE PLACE IS GONE!

GUARD THOSE EXITS!

IS THAT POWER-SHOVEL BOOM LONG ENOUGH TO REACH TRACY?

NOT A CHANCE.

WAS THE FIRE ALARM TURNED IN?

YES, BUT THIS PLACE IS GOING UP LIKE DRY TISSUE PAPER.

CHESTER GOULD

IT BURNED LIKE A DRY HAYSTACK!

THAT EXTENSION LADDER IS A GREAT THING! WHEW!

AS FOR FLATTOP—HE DIDN'T GET OUT. EVERY EXIT WAS COVERED BEFORE AND DURING THE FIRE.

THESE RUINS WILL COOL OFF FAST. THE BOYS ARE USING PLENTY OF WATER.

THEY'RE PUTTING A CHAIN ON FLATTOP'S "FABULOUS" CAR—TRYING TO GET IT OUT.

OKAY, TIGHTEN 'ER UP!

COMING OUT!

SO THAT'S WHAT'S LEFT?

H'M? THERE'S THE ICE BOX. AND I GUESS THAT'S THE TELEVISION SET.

LOOK AT THE PLUMBING! TRULY, THE GUY WAS CLEVER!

HEY!

THERE'S THE SAFE HANGING DOWN THERE. THE HEAT MUST HAVE MELTED THE BRACKETS AND LET IT DROP.

WE'LL HAVE THE TECHNICIANS OPEN IT IN THE LAB.

HOW SOON CAN WE PULL FLATTOP OUT OF THERE, CHIEF?

THE RUINS SHOULD BE COOL ENOUGH BY MORNING.

FLATTOP'S "WONDER" CAR, NOW A HEAP OF BLISTERED STEEL, GETS TOWED AWAY—

—AS POLICE PREPARE TO SEARCH THE BLACKENED RUINS FOR FLATTOP'S REMAINS.

THERE'S A BASEMENT ROOM BENEATH THIS STUFF. HERE'S A STAIRWAY.

AND IT'S FULL OF WATER. BETTER GET US A PUMP.

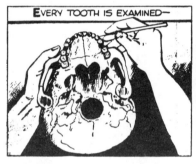

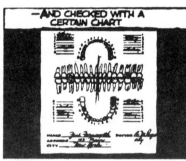

WHAT ARE YOU THINKING, TRACY?

I'M STUMPED.

WE'RE LOOKING FOR FLATTOP'S REMAINS, AND WE FIND THE BONES OF A HAM ACTOR! WHAT HAPPENED TO FLATTOP? HOW COULD SUCH A THING BE?

WHAT'S THAT?

AN OLD BRASS SPITOON—LOOKS LIKE.

AND BEER CANS.

THOSE AREN'T BEER CANS—WRONG SHAPE. THOSE ARE FOOD CANS! —DOZENS OF THEM.

THE THEATER SMOKING ROOM APPARENTLY WAS USED FOR LIVING QUARTERS BY THE OLD HAM ACTOR.

BUT HOW DID HE GET IN AND OUT?

IF WE KNEW THAT, CHIEF, WE'D KNOW WHAT HAPPENED TO FLATTOP.

SAM, CONTACT THE CITY HALL AND CHECK WITH THE FIRE DEPARTMENT. SEE IF YOU CAN LOCATE A FLOOR PLAN OF THIS OLD THEATER.

MR. TRACY, YOU HAVE A ROOKIE CLASS TO INSTRUCT AT THREE.

KEEP GUARDS HERE AND KEEP PEOPLE OUT. WE'RE NOT THROUGH WITH THIS PLACE.

WHAT HAPPENED TO FLATTOP?

WHAT HAPPENED TO FLATTOP? I CLAIM THE INTENSE HEAT OF THAT WOODEN STRUCTURE COMPLETELY CONSUMED HIM.

YOU'LL NEVER MAKE TRACY BELIEVE THAT, CHIEF.

I'LL SAY.

MEANWHILE, THE FLATTOP PROBLEM MOMENTARILY FORGOTTEN, TRACY DOES HIS STINT WITH THE ROOKIE CLASS.

THE POLICEMAN'S CLUB, OR BATON, CAN BE A VERY DANGEROUS WEAPON.

OR IT CAN BE USED AS AN INSTRUMENT OF FIRST AID—AS IN MAKING A TOURNIQUET TO STOP BLEEDING.

FURTHER USE OF THE POLICEMAN'S BATON INCLUDES WARDING OFF BLOWS FROM A KNIFE, BLACK-JACK, CLUB, BOTTLES, ETC.

NEVER PROBE YOUR PRISONER. HE HAS TWO FREE HANDS AGAINST YOUR ONE. YOU'LL LOSE YOUR CLUB.

ON THE OTHER HAND, TWO, OR EVEN THREE PRISONERS CAN BE HANDLED BY PROPER USE OF THE BATON.

YEAH—WHAT HAPPENED TO FLATTOP?

WORKING ALONE TODAY, SAM?

YEAH—KINDA.

A DIRTY MESS OF JUNK, ISN'T IT, MURPHY?

YES. WHAT HAVE YOU THERE? —A SURVEY?

UH-HUH— THAT OLD BRICK BUILDING ISN'T ON THE LINE, IS IT?

YOU MEAN IT'S OVER FROM WHERE IT OUGHT TO BE?

WELL, NOW, IT DOES LOOK LIKE THE THEATER AND THE BRICK BUILDING HAD ABOUT A FOOT BETWEEN THEM.

YOU GOT A SHOVEL?

98

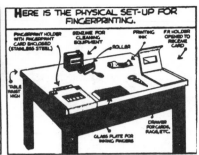

SURE, IT'S A THRESHOLD.

MURPHY, SEE WHAT THE DATE IS ON THE FRONT OF THIS BUILDING.

1904

OKAY.

THE OLD THEATER WAS BUILT SIXTEEN YEARS BEFORE THAT, IN 1888! — FOURTEEN INCHES INSIDE THE LOT LINE.

LATER, WHEN THE BRICK BUILDING WAS BUILT, THIS SIDE DOOR WAS ABANDONED.

—BUT THE DERELICT ACTOR USED IT TO GET TO HIS LIVING QUARTERS, AND THAT'S WHERE FLATTOP ESCAPED!

ZEUS FARNSWORTH STARRED IN OVER 30 PLAYS. THIS PICTURE WAS MADE IN THE TWENTIES, WHEN HE WAS AT HIS HEIGHT.

APPARENTLY, DURING THESE LATER YEARS, HIS HOME WAS THE BASEMENT ROOM OF THIS THEATER.

SOMEHOW, FLATTOP FOUND THAT ROOM **AND** THE **SIDE DOOR**.

FARNSWORTH MAY HAVE BEEN SLEEPING, AND FLATTOP NEVER EVEN BOTHERED TO WAKE HIM.

"BUT WHERE IS THAT FLAT-HEADED MORONIC JERK NOW?" ASKS THE CHIEF.

TURN LOOSE' QUIT CHOKING ME — GET OFF!

JIM—I JUST SAW A CRAZY MAN DOWN BY THE CREEK.

AW, GO ON.

NO KIDDING—HE WAS BEATING THE AIR WITH HIS FISTS AND JUMPING UP AND DOWN—HORRIBLE!

"AW—YOU JUST SAW ONE OF THEM POLITICAL CANDIDATES REHEARSING HIS SPEECH—THAT'S ALL YOU HEARD."

TURN LOOSE! QUIT CHOKING ME — TURN LOOSE!

GET OFF!

TURN LOOSE! (CHOKE)

NO, NO! TURN LOOSE! LET GO!

GET OFF MY BACK! QUIT CHOKING ME!

GET OFF!

THERE IS EVIDENCE OF A PATH—AND, I BELIEVE, A COUPLE OF FOOTPRINTS.

CREPE SOLES—LOOKS LIKE.

HAVE WE GOT THE CASTING KIT WITH US?

IT'S IN THE CAR.

AND SEVERAL MILES AWAY—

?

NO!

GET OFF MY BACK! TURN LOOSE!

IN HIS HEYDAY HE WAS THE COUNTRY'S GREATEST ACTOR. HE LIVED IN THE BASEMENT SMOKING ROOM OF THIS OLD THEATER, WHERE HE HAD STARRED IN PLAYS OVER 40 YEARS AGO.

FLATTOP USED HIS SECRET BASEMENT DOOR TO ESCAPE THE FIRE—WHILE THE OLD ACTOR WAS ASLEEP ON A COUCH.

AN ALCOHOLIC FOR YEARS, FARNSWORTH PROBABLY NEVER KNEW THE PLACE WAS AFIRE. FLATTOP COULD HAVE BOLTED PAST HIM WITHOUT EVEN SEEING HIM.

HEY!

TRACY, THE STATE POLICE WANT YOU TO COME OUT TO 96TH AND INDIAN ROAD TO SEE SOMETHING.

SEE SOMETHING?

SEEMS AS THOUGH THERE ARE SOME SCREWY FOOTPRINTS, AND A FANTASTIC STORY.

MEANWHILE—

I WORKED THIS FIELD DOWN FOR FALL PLANTING—AND I WAS COMING OUT WITH MY TRACTOR THIS MORNING WHEN I SAW HIM.

HE WAS GRABBING AT HIS NECK AND ROLLING ON THE GROUND—AND PUNCHING THE AIR! IT WAS TERRIBLE TO WATCH!

KEEP BACK—LET'S NOT DESTROY THOSE FOOTPRINTS.

HERE COMES TRACY.

TRACKS SHOW HE LEAPED AROUND AND THEN RAN TOWARD THE CREEK.

THE FARMER'S DESCRIPTION OF THIS BIRD TALLIES EXACTLY WITH FLATTOP!

BUT WHY THESE CRAZY ANTICS? HE MUST BE OFF HIS ROCKER!

AND HALF A MILE UPSTREAM

TURN LOOSE OF ME! GET OFF MY BACK!

QUIT CHOKING! TURN LOOSE—TURN LOOSE!

WE'VE BEEN UP AND DOWN BOTH SIDES OF THE STREAM. TRACKS GO IN, BUT NONE GO OUT.

HE COULD HAVE CLIMBED UP THAT GRAPEVINE.

—OR HE COULD HAVE WALKED OUT ON THOSE STONES.

"BUT WHO IS HE TRYING TO RUN AWAY FROM?" ASKS TRACY.

CLACKETY CLACK

SCRAPE IT OFF, TRAIN! SCRAPE IT OFF!

HEY!

GET OFF! LET GO!

I SAW IT ALL, BUT I DON'T BELIEVE IT.

NO, LIZZ. NOTHING NEW. FLATTOP'S JUST DISAPPEARED, THAT'S ALL. UMF, UH-UGH—

TALK ABOUT WOMEN BEING VAIN!

FOR HEAVEN'S SAKE, SAM, WILL YOU STOP MUMBLING SO I CAN UNDERSTAND YOU? AND QUIT COMBING YOUR HAIR!

RADIO ROOM

—COMBING MY HAIR? LOOK! WHAT WOULD YOU THINK IF I LEFT MY CHARMING, WAVY, RAVEN LOCKS IN DISARRAY IN YOUR PRESENCE?

OH, BROTHER! WHAT A POLICE DEPARTMENT!

WHY DON'T YOU GET A CREW-CUT?

OH! THAT CUT ME TO THE QUICK! YOU AND I, LIZZ, ARE THROUGH! WE HAVE REACHED AN ABYSS.

A CREW-CUT?

TELEVISION SHOW-UP

THIS NEXT GROUP IS FROM BUFFALO— COME IN, BUFFALO.

THERE'S NO FLATTOP THERE.

WHEN WILL CLEVELAND BE ON, FRANK?

NOT TILL 4 O'CLOCK, TRACY. WHY?

GOT A CW MESSAGE THAT A BERSERK GUY WAS PICKED UP THERE FOR RUNNING HIMSELF THROUGH A CAR-WASH MACHINE — AND I THOUGHT—

WELL, HOW DOES SHE LOOK?

YIPE!

ABSOLUTELY GREAT!

H'M? I NEVER FIGURED ON THIS.

COME TO THINK OF IT, MR. CATCHEM, I NEVER HEARD OF A DETECTIVE HAVING A CREW-CUT.

—AND I NEVER HEARD OF A CREW-CUT WEARING A HAT.

CAREFUL, GAL, THAT'S A FAMILY HEIRLOOM! BESIDES, IT'S WHERE I CARRY MY WIFE'S GROCERY LIST.

COOL, BOY— REAL COOL.

THE NEW JOB

LOOK, WE'RE MODERNIZING THE DEPARTMENT ALL AROUND! GET HEP! GET A CREW!

—OLD BUZZOM BUDDY AND SQUARE.

GET THAT MATTRESS STUFFING OFF YOUR FAT KNOB AND JOIN US CATS BEFORE IT'S TOO LATE.

GET YOUR GRUBBY HANDS OFF MY SAMPSON, YOU

WHAT ARE YOU THINKING, SON?

HEH, HEH, HEH!

SAM, JUNIOR TELLS ME YOU GOT A CREW-CUT. LET ME SEE IT.

YES, LIZZ, IT SEEMS I SET THE STYLE AROUND HERE! TRACY LIKES IT SO WELL HE'S IN THE BARBER SHOP GETTING ONE NOW.

HH, NO!

"THIS IS AN EARTH-SHAKING EVENT," SAYS LIZZ, "NOW, IF WE CAN JUST GET TRACY TO CHANGE HIS STYLE OF NECKTIE!"

HOW YOU LIKE?

OKAY, FRED-OKAY!

BRAVO! THIS IS AN EXCITING DAY—

Zing

SOMEBODY SHOOT MY WINDOW!

A STICK-UP JUST CLEANED OUT MY CASH REGISTER! HE WENT IN THAT SECOND DOOR!

I FIRED ONCE—OVER HIS HEAD—BUT I WAS AFRAID OF HITTING PEDESTRIANS.

—OVER HIS HEAD?

HUH??

WHO IS SHE?

DID SHE DO IT?

A STICK-UP MAN ROBBED MY BUTCHER SHOP. TRACY AND I WERE CHASING HIM, BUT WE DIDN'T SHOOT HIM.

SHE'S HOLDING AN AUTOMATIC, AND THAT MEANS IT'S COCKED FOR THE NEXT SHOT.

WHAT'LL WE DO?

103

PHOTOGRAPHING THE "MINUTE" CAMERA NEGATIVE GAVE US THIS EXCELLENT PICTURE, CHIEF.

WOW! SO THIS IS THE LITTLE GIRL'S MOTHER?

MUST BE! THE DEAD MAN'S PAROLE OFFICER REPORTS HE WAS MARRIED LAST DECEMBER TO A WOMAN WITH A LITTLE GIRL.

HONEY, IS THIS YOUR MOMMY?

NODDING YES

THEN, THIS PUTS LITTLE SPECS IN THE POSITION OF UNWITTINGLY HAVING SHOT HER STEPFATHER!

IMPOSSIBLE! THIS CHILD COULD NOT HAVE COCKED THIS AUTOMATIC, WITH ITS EIGHTEEN-POUND PULL. SOMEBODY DID IT FOR HER!

THERE **HAD** TO BE A THIRD PERSON IN THAT ROOM.

HONEY, WAS SOMEONE ELSE WITH YOU? THINK HARD, NOW— SOMEONE BESIDES YOU?

YES

SHE SHOOK HER HEAD YES!

LISTEN CAREFULLY NOW— DID THIS PERSON **HAND** YOU THE GUN?

YES

CAN YOU SHOW US HOW THIS PERSON HELPED YOU SHOOT THE GUN?

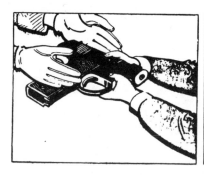

AM I SUPPOSED TO BE YOU?

YES

CHESTER GOULD

WELL, THERE IT IS! HER DEMONSTRATION MAKES IT ALL VERY CLEAR.

SOMEBODY STOOD BEHIND HER, HELD HER HANDS, AND FIRED THE GUN THAT KILLED HER STEPFATHER.

YES

THAT WOULD ELIMINATE FINGERPRINTS—EXCEPT THE CHILD'S.

WAS THAT PERSON WHO STOOD BEHIND YOU AND HELPED YOU HOLD THE GUN—YOUR MOTHER?

NO

CHESTER GOULD

TEMPORARILY, LITTLE SPEC IS GOING TO STAY WITH MY HUSBAND JIMMY AND ME. AREN'T YOU, SPEC?

SHE ANSWERED "OK."

I DIDN'T KNOW JIMMY THE REPORTER COULD TALK SIGN LANGUAGE.

CHIEF, IN MY BUSINESS YOU HAVE TO KNOW A LITTLE BIT ABOUT EVERYTHING!

SHALL WE GO, LIZZ?

MANY MILES FROM ALL THIS—

ARE YOU HAPPY, DARLING?

NEVER BEEN SO HAPPY IN MY LIFE!

HELLO, IVY.

HI, IVY.

WHAT ARE WE PRINTING TODAY, MARTY?

FIVES.

OH, BY THE WAY, I WANT YOU TO MEET MY WIFE! FLOSSIE, THIS IS MARTY.

H'LA

YES, IVY, THE PRESS IS WORKING GREAT! LOOK AT THIS NEW FIVE.

PERFECT!

WHO IS HE?

THIS IS RODNEY, OUR ENGRAVER. I OBTAINED A PAROLE FOR HIM, AND HE AND I BECAME CLOSE BUDDIES AND PARTNERS.

UH UH—

BUDDIES AND PARTNERS? —AND YOU HAVE HIM CHAINED?

CAN'T TAKE A CHANCE! HE'S TOO VALUABLE TO LET HIM GET AWAY, EH, RODNEY?

UH UH—

LOVE ME A LOT?

YES, IVY.

BOYLA BOOLA BOOLA BOOLA BOO-LA

FIRST, THE ROCKIES, THEN VEGAS, AND NOW THE SOUTHERN COAST! WHAT A WEEK WE'VE HAD, EH, DARLING!

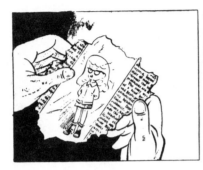

I CAN'T GET HER OUT OF MY MIND.

WHEN WE MADE OUR DEAL TO GET RID OF YOUR HUSBAND, WE AGREED IT WAS ALL OR NOTHING.

REMEMBER, YOU'RE AN ACCESSORY TO A MURDER.

I'M SORRY, IVY, YOU'RE RIGHT. I'M OKAY NOW. SHALL WE TAKE A WALK? THE NIGHT IS BEAUTIFUL.

YOU WON'T EVER DOUBLE-CROSS ME, WILL YOU, BABY?

WHILE BACK IN THE CITY, LIZZ HAS UNCOVERED AN IMPORTANT CLUE— THE OWNER OF THIS RESTAURANT IS A RETIRED POLO PLAYER.

CHESTER GOULD

I REMEMBERED THESE PICTURES FROM HAVING BEEN HERE WITH MY HUSBAND, JIMMY. LOOK AT THAT THIRD ONE.

IT'S HIM.

SURE, I KNOW IVY. GREAT HORSEMAN AND A CHAMPION POLO PLAYER— WHEN HE WAS YOUNGER.

—HAS A COUNTRY PLACE AND STABLES OUT ON ROUTE 20.

WHAT KIND OF FELLOW IS HE?

NEVER DID KNOW WHAT HE DID FOR A LIVING—BUT HE ALWAYS SEEMED WELL-HEELED. VERY SOLID CITIZEN.

AND HIGH OVER THE PACIFIC—

FLOSSIE! WHAT ARE YOU DOING?

CHESTER GOULD

SHE OUTWITTED ME— I PLANNED TO PUSH **HER.** SHE READ MY THOUGHTS---IT HAPPENED IN AN INSTANT---

SHARKS, SHARKS, SHARKS! HOW COULD I HAVE BEEN SO STUPID? HOW—??

MY NECKTIE AND A PIECE OF DRIFTWOOD—MY LIFE DEPENDS ON THIS TOURNIQUET.

WHERE CAN I GO? NOT BACK TO THE HOTEL— BUT WHERE—

I SAW A HOSPITAL IN THE LITTLE COAST TOWN AS WE PASSED THROUGH--- CAN'T BE MORE THAN A MILE---

TOUGH WALKING--- ROUGH BEACH---

APPROXIMATELY AN HOUR LATER—

I DO HAVE ONE SEAT ABOARD A SLOWER PLANE THAT LEAVES IN 20 MINUTES.

I'LL TAKE IT.

I'LL GO STRAIGHT TO THE POLICE— I'LL TELL THEM HE KIDNAPED ME--- HE TOOK ME FROM MY DAUGHTER. HE FORCED ME TO RUN AWAY—

THE BOLDNESS OF IT WILL MAKE IT CONVINCING! HE MURDERED MY HUSBAND—HE HELD ME PRISONER.

HE WON'T BE THERE TO DENY MY STORY. THEY **WILL** BELIEVE ME. I'LL REGAIN EVERYTHING, AND I'LL GET BACK MY DAUGHTER.

I---I MADE IT ASHORE, BUT I'M LOSING BLOOD---

BLACKIE! HERE, BLACKIE! WHATS HE BARK-ING AT?

HE'S BARKING AT THE MOON! DOGS LIKE TO BARK AT THE MOON.

THE MOON— MY EYE! THAT POOCH SEES SOMETHING!

117

118

THAT'S THE WHOLE STORY. I'VE TOLD YOU THE WHOLE TRUTH ABOUT IVY AND HIS COUNTERFEITERS.

YOU'LL BE KEPT IN PROTECTIVE CUSTODY TILL THIS IS CLEARED UP.

BASED ON THE WOMAN'S CONFESSION, TRACY AND SAM HAVE MOVED SWIFTLY.

JUST TWO.

THAT'S ALL.

THE REST MUST BE IN THE CAVE.

ACCORDING TO THE KID'S MOTHER— THIS IS THE HORSE THAT'S TRAINED TO OPEN THE CAVE.

WE'LL LET THE REINS HANG. SHE SAID THE HORSE WOULD KNOW WHERE TO GO.

AND SO, HEAVILY ARMED AND EQUIPPED WITH EXTRA AMMO AND TEAR GAS, THE DETAIL SETS OUT.

AND IN THE CAVE

FLATTOP DIDN'T SEE THE GUN I WAS HOLDING IN THE STRAP OF MY BAG. IT WAS EITHER HIS LIFE OR MINE.

SNOW WHITE HAIR

SO IVY GOT YOU PAROLED, ONLY TO KEEP YOU PRISONER?

UH UH

YOU SAY THERE'S NO WAY TO GET OUT TILL IVY OPENS THE CAVE DOOR?

MAYBE.— FOLLOW ME.

AND AS LIZZ FOLLOWS THE EX-CONVICT INTO THE DARKENED DEPTHS OF THE CAVE, AN APPARITION MIGHT BE SEEN RISING ABOVE THE FALLEN FLATTOP—

LAUGHTER ... THAT CANNOT BE HEARD.

AND THEN, QUIET ... FLATTOP IS FREE AT LAST!!

AH, HA, HA! YOU'VE PAID, FLATTOP!!— AT LAST, YOU'VE PAID!

AH, HA, HA, HA, HA, HA!

TRA, LA, LA, LA, LA HE PAID! HE PAID. TRA, LA!

MAIN DOOR CANNOT BE OPENED FROM INSIDE. THE ONLY WAY WE CAN GET OUT IS THIS UNDERGROUND RIVER.

UNDERGROUND RIVER?

AND LETTING THE HORSES MAKE THEIR OWN WAY, TRACY, SAM, AND THE OFFICERS RIDE ON.

DO YOU SUPPOSE THESE PLUGS KNOW WHERE THEY'RE GOING?

THE SEACOAST HOSPITAL, WHERE IVY HAS BEEN RECUPERATING.

BUT THE DOCTOR WILL BE FURIOUS—

I KNOW—BUT I'M LEAVING.

LOOK—THERE'S A GRAND—THAT SHOULD TAKE CARE OF MY BILL. GIVE THE DOC MY BEST—AND IT'S BEEN NICE KNOWING YOU.

AND BACK AT HEADQUARTERS.

AT LEAST, HE CAN NEVER SHOW UP TO DENY MY STORY HE'S GONE FOREVER—AND I HAVE MY CHILD.

WHILE AT THE CAVE—

FOR CRY-YI!

HEY, LOOK!

IT'S THE UNDERGROUND RIVER, OUR ONLY WAY OUT.

WAIT—

WAIT, RODNEY! I THOUGHT I HEARD A HORSE NEIGH! AND I THOUGHT I HEARD VOICES.

NO! WE DO NOT GO BACK.

THAT IS IVY RETURNING. BUT THIS TIME RODNEY WILL NOT BE THERE. THIS TIME RODNEY WILL ESCAPE FOR GOOD!

FLATTOP?

SHOT THROUGH THE HEAD!

BUT WHAT IS HE DOING HERE?

WE CAME HERE TO GET IVY AND HIS COUNTERFEITERS! WHAT TH—?

THIS CASE IS GETTING CRAZIER EVERY MINUTE!

THE PLACE SEEMS TO BE EMPTY OUTSIDE OF HIM.

MEANWHILE, LIZZ AND THE EX-CONVICT, RODNEY, CONTINUE ON THE UNDERGROUND RIVER.

WHERE WILL WE COME OUT?

JUST BELOW THE HILL NEAR THE RIDING STABLE.

SEE—WE ESCAPED! WE FREE! WORRIES OVER.

MAYBE YOURS ARE—NOT MINE.

RODNEY GO OTHER WAY. RODNEY NOT WAIT TO SEE IVY AGAIN—GOOD-BY.

WAIT!

ARE MY EYES DECEIVING ME? I CAN'T BELIEVE IT—BUT THAT LOOKS LIKE A SQUAD CAR!

CERTAINLY! WE WERE CALLED TO PICK UP A BODY—FLATTOP'S! BUT WHAT ARE YOU DOING HERE, LIZZ?

IF I TOLD YOU—YOU WOULDN'T BELIEVE IT!

WHILE TRACY AND HIS MEN ARE BUSY AT THE COUNTERFEIT CAVE, LET US VIEW AN INCIDENT NOW TAKING PLACE IN TOWN.

LOOK!

WHOSE CAR IS IT?

DON'T KNOW—TELL THE BOYS TO BRING THE EXTINGUISHER!

FIRE ACROSS THE STREET!

LET'S GO!

AS THE POLICE STATION PERSONNEL RUSH OUTSIDE, A FIGURE STANDS UNNOTICED NEAR THE ENTRANCE.

122

MURPHY, I THOUGHT I HEARD A **GUNSHOT** AS I CROSSED THE STREET.

WHAT'S ALL THE COMMOTION UPSTAIRS?

SO FAR, SO GOOD.

IT HAPPENED NOT MORE THAN TWO MINUTES AGO. SHE'S **DEAD!**

IF IT **WAS** IVY, HE'LL PROBABLY HEAD FOR THIS PLACE TO **HIDE OUT.**

WE'LL BE READY.

TAKE THE HORSES BACK AND PUT THEM IN THEIR STALLS JUST LIKE THEY WERE.

THEN STATION YOURSELVES IN HIS HOUSE WITH DRAWN GUNS AND WAIT. WE'LL DO THE SAME HERE.

AND IF YOU HAVE TO SHOOT, SHOOT TO KILL.

OKAY. LET'S TAKE OUR STATIONS AND WAIT FOR **IVY.**

HEY! RODNEY JUST THINK OF SOMETHING! **NITROGLYCERIN— IN VAULT**

12 GALLONS OF IT— WIRED ELECTRONICALLY! IVY CAN BLOW US ALL UP!

ELECTRONICALLY? ARE YOU KIDDIN'?

ME GET CROWBAR AND SHOW YOU NOT KIDDING! RODNEY OPEN DOOR AND DISCONNECT WIRE.

YE GADS! HE'S RIGHT!

SEE? **NITROGLYCERIN!** CAN BE SET OFF BY RADIO!

WHAT CAN WE DO?

MEANWHILE, IVY ARRIVES AT HIS STABLES—

THE PLACE IS ABANDONED. MY BOYS MUST **ALL** BE IN THE CAVE HAVING A BIG GAME! **THAT'S AGAINST MY ORDERS!**

I'D BETTER TAKE ALONG MY REMOTE CONTROL DETONATOR — JUST IN CASE!

BOOLA BOO-LA BOOLA BOO-LA

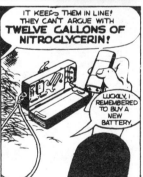

IT KEEPS THEM IN LINE! THEY CAN'T ARGUE WITH **TWELVE GALLONS OF NITROGLYCERIN!**

LUCKILY, I REMEMBERED TO BUY A NEW BATTERY.

IT'S A SEALED UNIT — CONNECTED TO A SHORT-WAVE SET

JUST ONE TOUCH OF THE WRONG WIRE — AND WE'RE GONERS!

RODNEY HELPED IVY INSTALL. RODNEY KNOW BEST HOW TO DISCONNECT.

"SAM JUST CALLED TO YOU FROM UPSTAIRS." SAYS LIZZ.

I HEARD A NOISE AT THE BIG DOOR

THE WHOLE THING WAS A RUSE TO EMPTY THE POLICE STATION WHILE HE SHOT HER.

HE MADE HIS ESCAPE DURING THE CONFUSION—IF HE HEADED YOUR WAY HE SHOULD ARRIVE SOON.

WE'RE ALL READY FOR HIM. **HOLD IT!** THE DOOR IS OPENING NOW.

HI, RODNEY! ITS ME.

BOOLA BOO-LA BOOLA BOO-LA

THERE ARE THREE OF US, IVY, **AND WE'VE ALL GOT MAGNUMS!**

WHAT A SURPRISE PARTY! BUT IT LOOKS LIKE WE'RE ALL IN THE SAME BOAT, GENTLEMEN.

SAME BOAT?

YES, THIS LITTLE DEVICE IS AN ELECTRONIC REMOTE CONTROL. I JUST NOW UNSNAPPED THE SAFETY.

AND THE SLIGHTEST MUSCULAR REACTION ON MY PART WILL RELEASE 12 GALLONS OF NITROGLYCERIN BURIED NOT TWENTY FEET FROM WHERE YOU'RE STANDING

FREEZE WHERE YOU ARE AND DROP THE GUNS.

I'M BACKING OUT, BUT YOU THREE ARE STAYING INSIDE.

WHILE UNKNOWN TO IVY, A FEVERISH EFFORT IS UNDER WAY BY LIZZ AND RODNEY IN AN ADJACENT CORRIDOR.

HAVE YOU FOUND THE RIGHT WIRE?

NOT SURE—BEEN SO LONG SINCE I HELP IVY INSTALL--- I FORGET.

THAT'S IT! DROP THE FIREARMS.

DON'T TACKLE ME OR HURL ANYTHING AT ME! REMEMBER, THE SLIGHTEST MUSCULAR REACTION WILL CAUSE ME TO RELEASE THIS BUTTON.

YOU ARE **DOOMED** GENTLEMEN, AND THERE'S **NOTHING** YOU CAN DO ABOUT IT!

AHA! AT LAST! **I HAVE FOUND THE RIGHT WIRE!** HAND ME THOSE PLIERS.

MISS EGGHEAD'S REVENGE

PRINCIPAL PERPETRATORS: **Miss Egghead;
the Dropper**

*ORIGINALLY APPEARED: July 23, 1958–
December 21, 1958*
WRITER/ARTIST: Chester Gould

The Miss Egghead continuity is a long one, and this concluding sequence is in effect that story's own sequel, as the murderess and her accomplice attempt to murder the detective by airplane.

This distinctive set piece—in which Tracy is literally stranded on a deserted island (actually, *inside* a *nearly* deserted island)—was the highlight of one of Gould's most honored periods: In 1959, the cartoonist won the first of his two National Cartoonist Society Reuben awards. "Dick Tracy" remains the only story strip to be so-honored. (Milton Caniff won two Reubens; however, one was for "Terry and the Pirates," and the other was for "Steve Canyon.")

Dick Locher—the coeditor of this volume and current "Dick Tracy" artist—was one of Gould's art assistants when this story was produced. Locher and the rest of Gould's staff—brother Ray Gould, the letterer; and Al Valanis, the ex-police artist responsible for researching and drawing the "Crimestopper's Textbook" Sunday featurette—participated in Monday morning story conferences.

Gould described his plotting as "fly by the seat of your pants" and never knew ahead of time how he was going to get Tracy out of a scrape. It was in these story conferences that Tracy got in, and out, of trouble. Locher, a pilot and aeronautics buff, came up with the up-to-date (if *deus ex machina*) solution for the canyon situation.

-YES, WUNBROW, OUR GIRL WAS OVERHEARD TO CONTACT A MAN NAMED CHICORY. WHO IS CHICORY, AND WHERE—?

CHICORY? CHICORY? AHA, YES! HE'S A GAMECOCK BREEDER AND GENERAL UNDERCOVER CONTACT MAN. BUT WHAT—

WHERE'S HE LOCATED?

NOW, SPEAK CLEARLY INTO THE MIKE, MISS EGGHEAD, AND ANSWER ALL QUESTIONS.

AS I UNDERSTAND IT, THE POLICE ARE AFTER YOU AND YOU WANT TO LEAVE CUBA BY PLANE.

YES.

TWO-WAY MIRROR

CHICORY SENT ME. HE SAID YOU WOULD HELP ME.

THAT DEPENDS! WE DO BUSINESS WITH A VERY RESTRICTED CLIENTELE.

I MUST FLEE CUBA IMMEDIATELY! CHICORY SAID YOU HAD A PLANE.

I DO. I HAVE A FLEET OF TWO-MOTOR CONVERS.

A FLIGHT TO YOUR HOME TOWN WILL COST YOU ONE THOUSAND DOLLARS—TAKE IT OR LEAVE IT.

ONE THOUSAND DOLLARS?

I HAPPEN TO KNOW WHO YOU ARE, MISS EGGHEAD, AND I ALSO KNOW SOMETHING ELSE THAT MAY INTEREST YOU.

WHAT IS THAT?

DICK TRACY IS IN CUBA FOR THE EXPRESS PURPOSE OF PICKING YOU UP FOR MURDER.

HOW DID YOU KNOW THAT? WHO ARE YOU?

IT'S MY BUSINESS TO KNOW THINGS. SHALL I BOOK YOU FOR A SIX O'CLOCK FLIGHT?

YES. WHEN DO I PAY?

HAVE THE CASH WITH YOU AT THE AIRPORT. NOW, WILL YOU PLEASE REMOVE YOUR HOOD FOR 10 SECONDS?

—AND LOOK INTO THE MIRROR.

GOOD—NOW, PUT THE HOOD BACK.

SNAP

CLICK

THE ATTENDANT WILL TELL YOU HOW TO REACH OUR PRIVATE AIRPORT. BE THERE AT 5:45. THAT IS ALL.

MEANWHILE—

YES, MY NAME IS CHICORY AND I RAISE GAMECOCKS, BUT WHEN IT COMES TO BEING A STOOL PIGEON, I NO SPICK THE LANGUAGE.

NO SPICK THE LANGUAGE, EH?

THE GRAPEVINE TELLS ME THIS WOMAN VISITED YOU NOT MORE THAN AN HOUR AGO—OH—

CLACK

OH—THIS LANGUAGE YOU SPICK —EH? WELL, LET'S TALK.

135

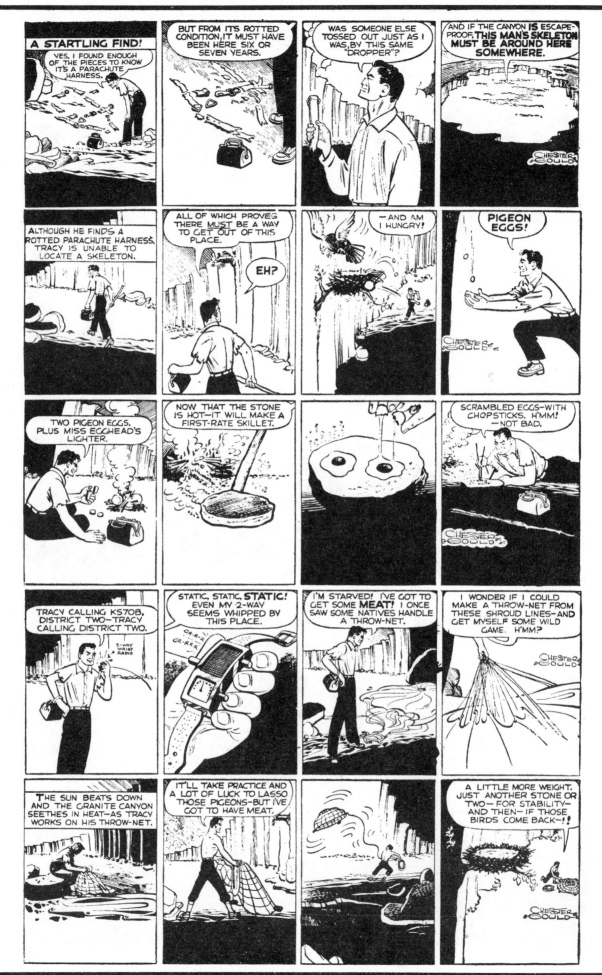

THERE—IT HANDLES BETTER, NOW.

THIS CANYON SEEMS ABSOLUTELY DEVOID OF GAME LIFE—EXCEPT FOR THOSE WILD PIGEONS. **AND THEY'VE FLOWN AWAY—**

HUH? THEY'RE BACK?

BRU-THER! I'VE GOT TO GET 'EM ON THE FIRST TRY. THE NUMBER-ONE TOSS MUST BE A BULL'S-EYE.

CHESTER GOULD

DESPERATELY TRYING TO BEAT THE SPECTRE OF STARVATION, TRACY HAS FASHIONED A THROW-NET FROM THE SHROUD LINES OF HIS PARACHUTE IN AN ATTEMPT TO CAPTURE SOME WILD GAME.

I ONCE SAW SOME NATIVES HANDLE ONE OF THESE THINGS—BUT IT WAS **SECOND NATURE** WITH THEM.

THOSE WILD PIGEONS ARE THE ONLY GAME I'VE SEEN—AND THEY'RE 25 FEET UP—

IT'S GOING TO TAKE SOME PRACTICE —BECAUSE THOSE BIRDS WILL BE ON THE WING AFTER THE FIRST CAST.

TRACY PICKS OUT CERTAIN STONES AND BUSHES—AND CONTINUES TO PRACTICE LAYING THE NET OVER THEM.

THAT NYLON WILL TAKE A LOT OF PUNISHMENT. THIS PRACTICE WON'T HURT IT—

HUH?

IS THAT THE MAN THE PARACHUTE HARNESS BELONGED TO—THAT IS, THE ROTTED FRAGMENTS THAT I FOUND? IS HE THE OWNER?

A VINE! HE TRIED TO CLIMB OUT ---THE VINE BROKE---HE DIED WHERE HE FELL.

THE VINE CONTINUED TO GROW— GAD! THAT MUST HAVE HAPPENED SEVERAL YEARS AGO.

ALL OF WHICH WOULD SEEM TO PROVE THIS PLACE IS **ESCAPE-PROOF!**

CHESTER GOULD

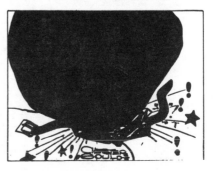

144

145

146

LOCKED IN HIS BASEMENT WITH THE GAMECOCKS! WHY, THAT—!!

BUT YOU CANNOT KEEP HER DOWN THERE FOREVER, CHICORY.

FOREVER? NO. BUT UNTIL I FIGURE OUT WHAT TO DO WITH HER $50,000, YES.

NOBODY CAN DO THIS TO AN EGGHEAD AND GET AWAY WITH IT, YOU COMMON CUT-THROATS!

LOCKED IN YOUR DIRTY BASEMENT WITH YOUR FILTHY GAMECOCKS! LET ME OUT!

MISS EGGHEAD'S MAKING MORE NOISE THAN THE HURRICANE, CHICORY. WHAT ABOUT IT?

SHE CAN'T BREAK THROUGH THAT STEEL MESH. LET HER YELL.

HEY, GORILLA! THIS COULD TURN INTO A TIDAL WAVE. WE MAY HAVE TO ABANDON THIS PLACE. NO KIDDIN', CHICORY!

THE SAME HURRICANE THAT LASHES CHICORY'S MANSION ALSO RELEASES A DELUGE OF WATER ON THE ISLAND PRISON OF TRACY AND WHITEHALL.

WELL, WE WANTED OUR "S.O.S." LETTERS FILLED UP. HA! THEY'RE FILLED, ALL RIGHT. YES, YOU CAWN'T EVEN SEE THEM.

MAYBE IF ENOUGH WATER FALLS TO FILL THIS CANYON WE CAN SWIM OUT, WHITEHALL. OLD CHAP, YOUR HUMOR IS ALWAYS WITH YOU, EH, WOT?

ONE THING'S SURE. OUR ROOF DOESN'T LEAK—AND WE'VE NO PLANS FOR A GARDEN PARTY TONIGHT, SO— LET 'ER RAIN.

LET ME OUT OF HERE, YOU—

PLEASE, MISS EGGHEAD, YOU ASKED US TO HIDE YOU FROM THE POLICE. NOW WHO WOULD LOOK FOR YOU IN A GAMECOCK PEN IN MY BASEMENT?

AND WHILE WE'RE FEEDING THE GAMECOCKS, I MIGHT AS WELL TAKE YOUR ORDER FOR SUPPER. DO YOU LIKE YOUR STEAK RARE, MEDIUM OR WELL?

CHICORY, COME QUICK!

IT MUST HAVE BLOWN IN UNDER THE DOOR. BLOWN IN?? WAIT— I'LL SHOW YOU!

CLOSE IT, GORILLA! THE WATER'S SIX INCHES DEEP OUT THERE

PUT THE GAMECOCKS IN BAGS. WE'VE GOT TO GET OUT OF HERE.

I SAID WE'RE TAKING OUR GAMECOCKS OUT. UH-UH— IS THAT WATER?

TEMPORARILY CALM HERE, BUT WE UNDERSTAND THE STORM'S STILL RAGING. UP AHEAD. HOWEVER, WE'RE COMING TO CUBA WITH TRACY AND WHITEHALL.

BREAD! JUST GOOD OLD BREAD!

HOW ABOUT A LITTLE ROAST BEEF?

"TRACY, OLD BOY, AS SOON AS WE'VE REGAINED OUR STRENGTH, SUPPOSE WE GO TOPSIDE AND KISS THAT NOSE CONE," SAYS WHITEHALL.

MEANWHILE, BACK WHERE THE HURRICANE STILL RAGES, MISS EGGHEAD SITS ABANDONED IN CHICORY'S FLOODED BASEMENT.

IT'S RISING-- EVERY MINUTE IT'S RISING!

I NEVER KNEW BEEF COULD BE SO GOOD, EH, WHITEHALL?

RIGHTO! ANOTHER PIECE OF THAT BEEF, IF YOU PLEASE.

WE SENT MESSAGES TO YOUR RESPECTIVE HOME OFFICES, GENTLEMEN.

ALSO WE REQUESTED THAT YOUR FAMILIES BE GIVEN THE GOOD NEWS OF YOUR RESCUE.

FURTHERMORE, HERE'S A TELEPHONE. YOU MAY TALK TO YOUR WIVES DIRECT, IF YOU WISH.

---FROM NOW ON, TESS. I'LL ALWAYS HAVE A WARM PLACE IN MY HEART FOR MISSILE NOSE CONES---

HONEY, BONNIE BRAIDS WANTS TO SAY HELLO.

---"BOTH TRACY AND WHITEHALL ABOARD CRASH BOAT 267 HEADED FOR HAVANA. HEALTH GOOD--BOTH WILL BE TAKEN TO CENTRAL HOSPITAL HAVANA, FOR CHECK-UP."

CHIEF, HOW ABOUT MY TAKING AN AFTERNOON PLANE TO CUBA? I'D LIKE TO BE THERE WHEN HE ARRIVES.

GREAT, SAM!

YOU SEE, DROPPER, THAT FLOODING BASEMENT OF MINE WILL FINISH MISS EGGHEAD. LATER WHEN WE RETURN TO THE HOUSE, WE'LL SPIRIT THE BODY TO A PUBLIC PARK WHERE IT CAN BE FOUND.

AND MISS EGGHEAD WILL BE JUST ANOTHER DROWNING VICTIM OF THE HURRICANE.

I DON'T LIKE IT!

CHICORY, GO BACK AND FINISH THE JOB! SUPPOSE RESCUE PARTIES FIND THE BODY BEFORE YOU GET IT OUT?

HA! DON'T KID YOURSELF. RESCUERS WILL BE TOO BUSY IN THE LOWER SECTIONS OF TOWN TO CHECK MY PLACE.

AND MISS EGGHEAD FACES HER FATE, PANIC-STRICKEN AND HORRIFIED.

THAT WAS A FOOTSTEP! I KNOW IT WAS A FOOTSTEP ON THE FLOOR ABOVE.

IS SOMEONE COMING TO SAVE ME??

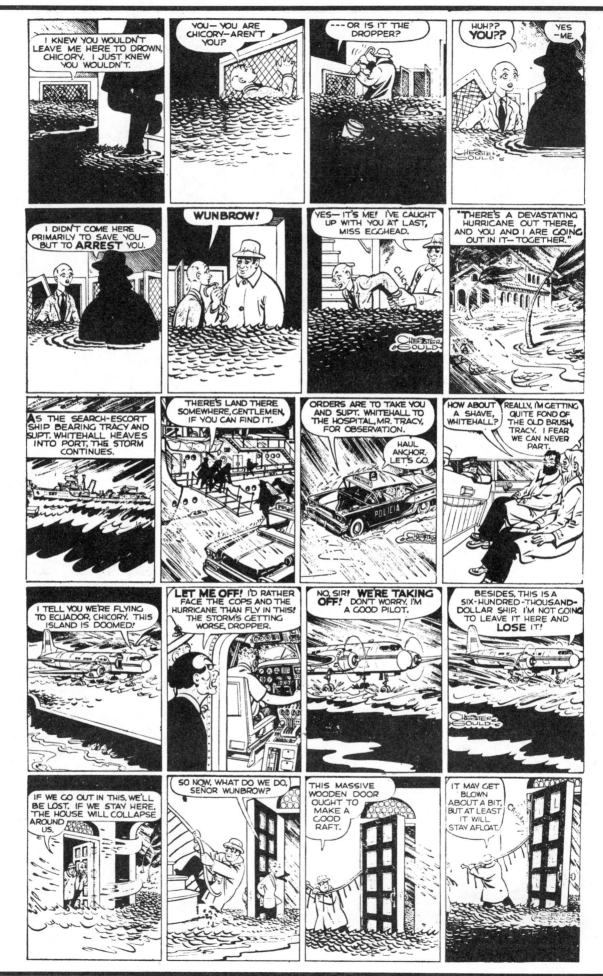

151

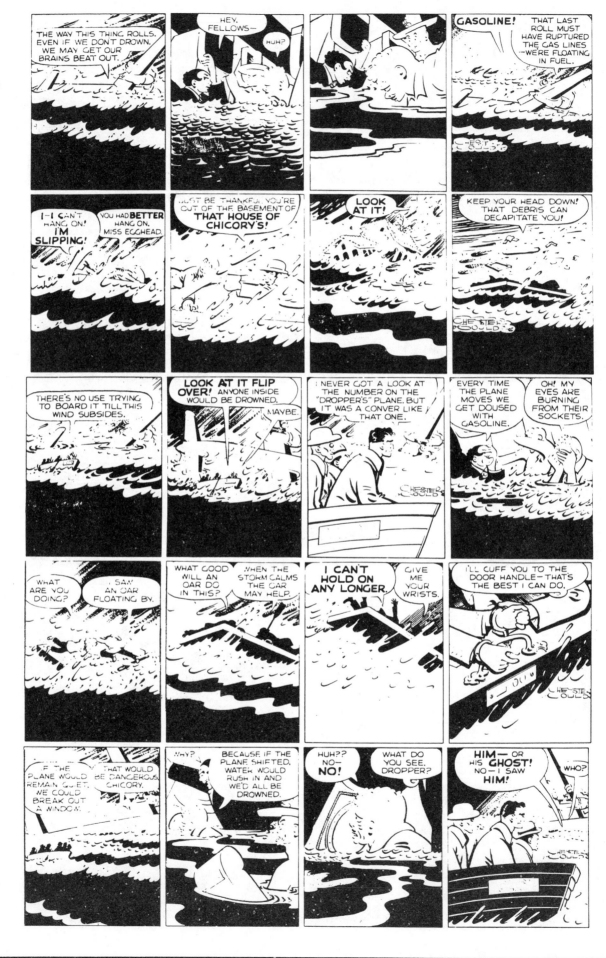

THE DOOR WITH ITS HUMAN CARGO BOBS AND BOUNCES AS THE STORM RAGES.

THEN IT FLIPS OVER!

MISS EGGHEAD!

FLAPS DOWN SHOWS THE PLANE WAS TRYING TO TAKE OFF.

AND THE BENT PROPELLOR BLADES PROVE THE MOTORS WERE RUNNING WHEN SHE CRASHED!

NOW THE QUESTION IS—WHO'S INSIDE AND ARE THEY STILL ALIVE?

THERE'S ONE WAY WE CAN FIND OUT. THE PLANE SHIFTED A MINUTE AGO SO THAT THE TAIL DOOR IS EXPOSED. LET'S GO.

WE'VE GOT TO WATCH IT, BOYS —I SMELL GASOLINE.

BEFORE THE FUSILAGE TURNED, I GOT ONE LAST GLANCE THROUGH THE WINDOW. IT'S DICK TRACY AND THE POLICE!

IT CAN'T BE DICK TRACY.

IT IS DICK TRACY AND THAT ENGLISHMAN, WHITEHALL, THAT I DUMPED LAST MARCH.

HOW DID—??

MAYBE IT'S A GOOD THING THEY'RE COMING. THESE GAS FUMES WOULD KILL US ANYWAY.

THE DIRTY COPPERS WILL NEVER GET ME.

DON'T FIRE THAT GUN!! —THESE GAS FUMES—

SWIM FOR YOUR LIVES, BOYS, INTO THE WIND.

154

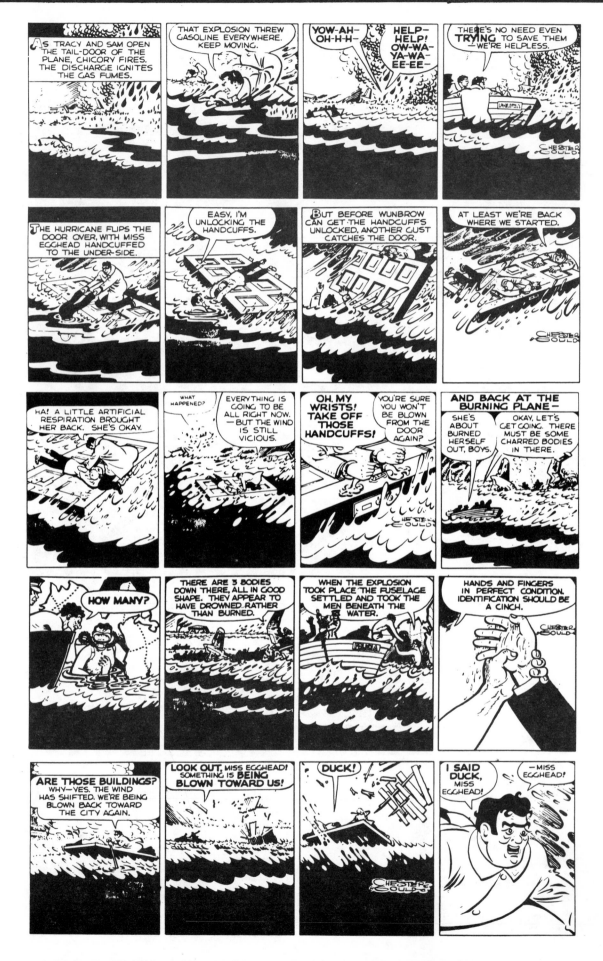

FINGERPRINT ALL THREE AND GET COPIES TO THE FBI VIA THE SPEEDPHOTO MACHINE. I HAVE A HUNCH THESE BOYS WERE BIG TIME.

WELL DOES THAT DO IT, TRACY?

I'M GOING TO TAKE ONE MORE LOOK, SAM.

YES, THE "DROPPER" AND CHICORY AND THE "GORILLA" GOT WHAT WAS COMING TO THEM. IT'S TOO BAD ALL CRIMINAL RATS CAN'T FINISH THEMSELVES OFF LIKE THAT.

RIGHTO.

"NOW IF WE COULD JUST ACCOUNT FOR MISS EGGHEAD, WE'D HAVE THE WHOLE BUNCH," OBSERVES SAM.

155

AFTER THE EXPLOSION THE BODIES WERE CARRIED BENEATH THE SURFACE AS THE FUSELAGE SETTLED. CONSEQUENTLY, THEY WERE NOT BURNED TO DEATH — BUT DROWNED.

THE FBI IDENTIFIED THEM THROUGH FINGERPRINTS. TWO OF THEM WERE INTERNATIONAL HOODLUMS—WANTED IN THE U.S.A. AND A COUPLE OF SOUTH AMERICAN COUNTRIES.

THAT'S ALL WE CAN DO HERE. LET'S GO.

LATER AT THE POLICE MORGUE.

THE "DROPPER'S" REAL NAME WAS NED GARMARR. HE WAS AN AMERICAN FLYER WHO LATER GOT INTO "ONE-WAY" OCEAN-RIDE BUSINESS FOR THE UNDERWORLD.

HOW MISS EGGHEAD MADE CONTACT WITH HIM, WE CAN ONLY SURMISE.

AND SPEAKING OF MISS EGGHEAD REMINDS ME OF WUNBROW. WHAT'S THE LATEST?

ALL WE KNOW, TRACY, IS THAT WUNBROW INSISTED ON GOING TO CHICORY'S HOUSE DURING THE STORM. HE SAID HE HAD A HUNCH.

A HUNCH? WHAT HUNCH?

HE WOULDN'T SAY. WE COULDN'T TALK HIM OUT OF IT AND YOU KNEW WUNBROW, HE HAD HIS WAY.

HE'S A STUBBORN ONE.

CUBA'S GREATEST DETECTIVE—BUT HE TOOK TOO MANY CHANCES.

WHY DON'T YOU FELLOWS GET BACK TO YOUR HOTEL AND GET SOME REST?

NOW THAT THE STORM IS SUBSIDING, EVERY POLICE BOAT, AS WELL AS THE COAST GUARD CRAFTS, WILL BE LOOKING FOR WUNBROW.

HEY— HUH??

WHAT IN—??

NO! IT'S A MIRAGE.

—ISN'T IT?

WUNBROW!

SALUDO.

MISS EGGHEAD??

YES, IT'S A LONG STORY! DO YOU WANT TO HEAR IT?

A WOMAN SCORNED

PRINCIPAL PERPETRATORS: **The Mole; Molene; the Pouch; Johnny Scorn**

ORIGINALLY APPEARED: March 7, 1971– August 15, 1971
WRITER/ARTIST: Chester Gould

Those who dismiss Chester Gould's last decade and a half, because of dislike for the infusion of science-fiction elements into the strip, should consider the continuity that follows as an Exhibit for the Defense.

Gould may not have been at his most focused, disciplined best in this period, but his imagination remained as fertile as ever. And his artwork is distinctively Chester Gould—that wonderfully skewed combination of realism and expressionism that so amused and impressed the Pop Art crowd.

Wildly conceived characters practically tumble from these panels. The resurfacing of one of Gould's greatest villains—the Mole—rates only a subplot in this energetic tale. A female terrorist—in most crime stories, a vivid central figure—is relegated to a bit part. A villain grotesque even for Chester Gould—the Pouch—gets away with murder.

At the same time, Gould drives home his pro-police viewpoint, so characteristic of this period, and seems as sharp as ever in presenting up-to-date police procedure.

But what impresses most about this tale is the offbeat black humor—Molene showering while wearing a gun-belt—and the extravagant, almost capricious twists of plot. When Chester Gould is plotting by the seat of his pants, we best all buckle up our seat belts—it's going to a wonderfully bumpy ride.

By the way, policewoman Lizz—you will note —is dark-haired, here. Gould darkened her hair from blonde to black, in the early sixties, possibly to keep her from being mistaken for Dick's wife, Tess (whose place, in a way, Lizz had taken, in terms of being actively involved in adventures . . . once married, Tess stayed home and out of harm's way, for the most part).

And Lizz's husband, Jimmy—seen in the 1956 continuity published herein—pretty much vanished from the strip, almost immediately. Frankly, Chet seemed to have forgotten about him—although an occasional passing reference indicates reporter Jimmy died that rarest of "Dick Tracy" deaths: a nonviolent, offstage one.

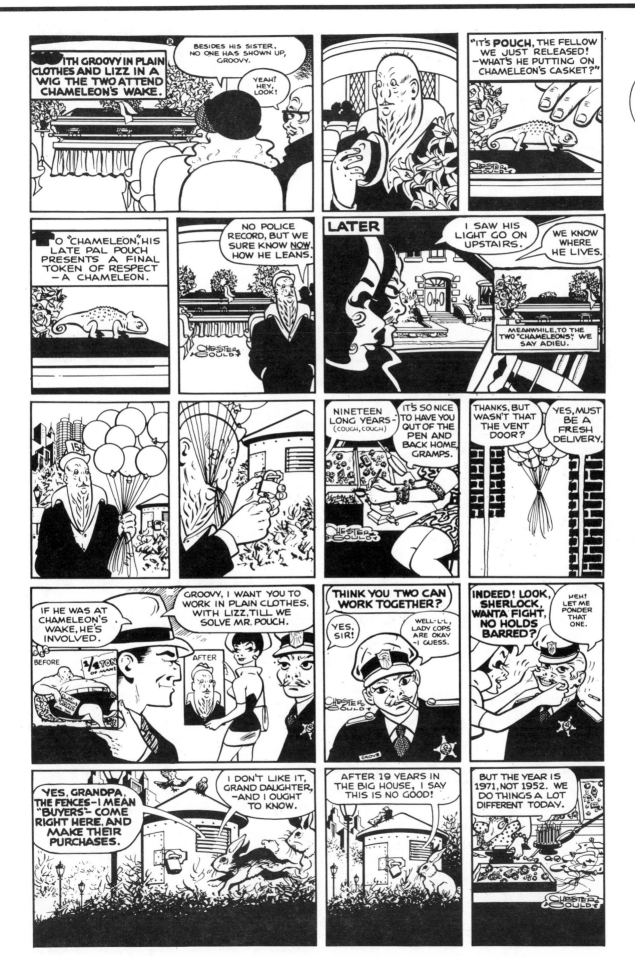

YES, GRANDDAUGHTER, 19 YEARS IN THE BIG HOUSE CAN SURE RUIN YOUR HEALTH.

OH, MY ARTHRITIS.

POP

GRANDPA MOLE, I'LL CHEER YOU UP IN JUST A MINUTE.

LOOK! A FIVE CARAT BLUE WHITE!

YAH! BUT I DON'T TRUST POUCH! HE'S TOO CARELESS. THIS SET-UP IS TOO CORNY! WHY DON'T YOU GO STRAIGHT, GRANDDAUGHTER?

THAT NIGHT LIZZ AND GROOVY CONTINUE THEIR ASSIGNMENT.

YEAH, THIS MASTER KEY FITS THE PADLOCK.

WAIT—HERE HE COMES.

I'LL TAKE OVER. HE KNOWS YOU, LIZZ.

HOW ABOUT A B'LOON, OLD MAN? (HIC)

GET AWAY, WINO! THESE ARE SOLD.

AW, C'MON.

AS GROOVY PRESSES HIS ACT, ONE OF THE BALLOONS PUNCTURES ON A LOW HANGING TWIG.

WITH THE ENSUING BURST, AN OBJECT FLYS THROUGH THE AIR, SHINING BRIGHTLY IN THE LIGHT OF THE STREET LAMP.

POP

WHEREUPON THE POUCH RELEASES THE REMAINING BALLOONS!

CHESTER GOULD

A TWIG PIERCED ONE AND THE RING FLEW OUT! THEY ALL MUST CONTAIN DIAMONDS.

VERY CUNNING! YOU LET THE EVIDENCE FLOAT AWAY, EH, POUCH?

YEAH. WHAT CAN YOU PROVE NOW?

ANYWAY, I'D CLAIM A FRAME-UP, AND WHO'D BELIEVE HER STORY ABOUT DIAMONDS IN A BALLOON? GLOATS POUCH.

CHESTER GOULD

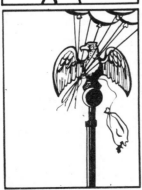

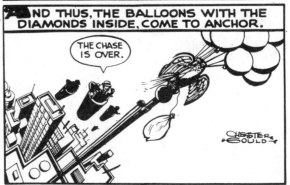

TEN-ABOVE ZERO TEMPERATURE KEPT THE GAS IN THE BALLOONS FROM EXPANDING AND TAKING THEM TO HIGHER ALTITUDES.

YES, SAM, AND TO TOP IT OFF THEY GET SNAGGED BY THE AMERICAN EAGLE!

"LIKE LIZZ SAID, THEY'RE LOADED WITH EVIDENCE. HEAR THEM RATTLE?"

ONE OF THE CLEVEREST TRICKS I'VE EVER SEEN TO TRANSPORT CONTRABAND.

BACK IN THE PARK—

AFTER I SHOT HIS GUN FROM HIS HAND, POUCH JUST DISAPPEARED.

I SAW HIM REACH FOR HIS NECK —AND I RECALLED THAT LAST WEEK I SAW WHAT APPEARED TO BE THE OUTLINE OF AN AUTOMATIC UNDER HIS SKIN.

LIZZ, YOUR MARKSMANSHIP IS SUPERB. I FEAR FOR THE SECOND TIME I'VE FAILED TO BE A GOOD COP. HAD YOU NOT SHOT THIS WEAPON FROM HIS HAND—

YES, ONCE AGAIN YOU APPROACHED A SUSPECT WITH YOUR GUN IN ITS HOLSTER.

AND TRACY WARNED ME!

POUCH'S GUN

"AFTER ALL", MOANS GROOVY, "HE SEEMED LIKE A HARMLESS OLD MAN!"

AS THE TWO TURN TO LEAVE, A PORTION OF GROOVY'S JACKET CATCHES ON A BUSH.

I THOUGHT—

YOU THOUGHT WHAT?

I THOUGHT I HEARD A DOOR SHUT.

A DOOR SHUT?

WE'RE NOT NEAR ANY BUILDINGS.

BALLOONS, POPCORN, CIGARETTES, COLD BEER—

—DIAMONDS!

RATTLE RATTLE

YEAH, THEY'VE GONE.

BUT I TELL YOU, MOLE, THIS PLACE ISN'T SAFE.

POUCH, YOU'RE A FOOL! YOU AND MOLENE ARE BOTH FOOLS. I'M STAYING RIGHT HERE.

AFTER LIZZ SHOT POUCH'S GUN OUT OF HIS HAND, HE JUST DISAPPEARED.

FINE DETECTIVES YOU TWO! YOU WORKED LIKE REAL AMATEURS.

WHAT'S CAUGHT ON YOUR SLEEVE, GROOVY?

A TWIG. I MUST HAVE PICKED IT UP IN THE PARK.

KINDA EARLY IN THE SPRING FOR GREEN FOLIAGE ISN'T IT?

IT WAS MORE OF A DULL THUD?

TO ME, IT SOUNDED LIKE A DOOR SLAM.

WHEN YOU HEARD IT HAD POUCH **ALREADY** DISAPPEARED?

YES.

WHAT ARE YOU DOING TO THAT TWIG TRACY?

I THOUGHT YOU'D NEVER ASK.

THIS TWIG, CAUGHT ON GROOVY'S SLEEVE, IS **PLASTIC.**

CLACK CLACK CLACK

WHAT? A PLASTIC BUSH IN THE PARK?

SEARCH WARRANT

+

PLASTIC TWIG

=

I DIDN'T WANT TO SAY ANYTHING TO GROOVY AND LIZZ, BUT THEY'VE HIT THE FIRST PAY DIRT OF THIS CASE.

IF GROOVY'S COAT SLEEVE CAUGHT THIS "TWIG" IN THE PARK—

JUST WHEN DID THE PARK BOARD START SETTING OUT **PLASTIC** BUSHES?

AND WHERE?

NIGHT – AND A RAINY ONE AT THAT!

IS THAT COOKING I SMELL? NYA! HOW COULD ANYBODY COOK IN ONE OF THOSE OLD AIR SHAFTS?

"WOULD POUCH HAVE CONFEDERATES??"

I MUST BE CRAZY. GROOVY LIKELY CAUGHT THIS PLASTIC TWIG IN SOME STORE.

CONTRABAND FOUND IN THE BALLOONS SET AFLOAT BY POUCH HAS MADE HIM THE MOST WANTED CRIMINAL OF THE HOUR.

BUT WHERE IS POUCH?

GROOVY AND LIZZ SAID HE JUST DISAPPEARED. YEAH? NOBODY JUST DISAPPEARS.

BESIDES, I CAN SMELL THE ODOR OF COOKING MEAT COMING FROM THIS VENT.

GROOVY HAD LEFT FOR THE DAY BEFORE I DISCOVERED THAT THIS TWIG CAUGHT ON HIS SLEEVE BUTTON WAS ARTIFICIAL –PLASTIC.

A PLASTIC BUSH –WHAT WOULD A PLASTIC BUSH BE DOING IN THE PARK?

AND NOT FAR BELOW GROUND.

I TELL YOU, MOLENE, YOU AND GRANDPA MOLE HAVE GOT TO GET OUT OF THIS HOLE–

I'M NOT HUNGRY.

SH-SH, LISTEN.

CLOMP CLOMP CLOMP CLOMP

HA! IT'S THE ONLY GREEN BUSH, AND IT'S PLASTIC WILD PLUM–MATCHES THE TWIG.

WHAT?

CHESTER GOULD

DON'T TOUCH THAT GUN. KEEP EATING.

MOLE, ARE YOU NUTS?

KEEP EATING!

CHESTER GOULD

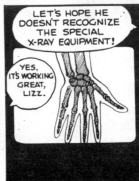

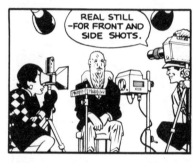

SO YOU SEE, CHIEF, HOW THE HANDS OF THE POLICE ARE TIED.

I KNOW.

ESCALATOR

"UNLESS A DIAMOND IS X-RAYED AND REGISTERED, IT IS VIRTUALLY UNIDENTIFIABLE."

THIS ELECTRIC FURNACE SHOWS HOW THEY DESTROYED THE SETTINGS BY MELTING THEM DOWN BUT—WE FOUND NO INGOTS.

THE GUN FOUND ON THE MOLE IS MOLENE'S—HIS DAUGHTER—AND IS REGISTERED IN HER NAME.

SHE CLAIMS SHE'S BEEN INVESTING HIS SAVINGS, LEFT BEHIND 19 YEARS AGO, IN THE DIAMOND TRADE. WHAT CRUD! WHAT NERVE!

THIS HAS TO BE A MUSICAL COMEDY.

WE MUST BE ABLE TO PROVE EVERY POINT.

"UNDER PRESENT LAWS WE MAY EVEN HAVE TO RETURN MOLE'S 'PROPERTY' TO HIM."

AND IT'S NO MUSICAL COMEDY.

COURT RULINGS WOULD INDICATE WE HAVEN'T ENOUGH PROOF AT THIS TIME TO MAKE A FORMAL CHARGE.

EVEN POUCH IS BEING RELEASED ON BOND THOUGH HE WAS CARRYING A CONCEALED WEAPON IN HIS DEWLAP!

YES, UNDER TODAY'S INTERPRETATION OF THE LAWS, IT SEEMS IT'S THE POLICE WHO ARE HANDCUFFED!

CHESTER GOULD

AND THAT'S THE LAW!

THEY'RE FREE!—NOT ONLY THAT BUT WE HAD TO RETURN THEIR "PROPERTY"!

TRACY, THE DIAMOND REGISTRATION BUREAU WANTS YOU ON THE CLOSED CIRCUIT.

10-4.

CHESTER GOULD

WE'VE IDENTIFIED 6 OF THE STONES AS STOLEN, TRACY. YOU NOW HAVE A CASE!

LEGAL LOOPHOLES, PLUS INABILITY TO IDENTIFY PROPERTY AS STOLEN AND PROVE A CRIME HAS BEEN COMMITTED, HAS SO FAR MADE A SHAMBLES OF THE CASE AGAINST MOLE AND MOLENE.

THEIR ATTORNEY'S GETTING A WRIT OF REPLEVIN—FOR THOSE SPARKLERS—WAS THE LAST STRAW.

OUR NET GAIN IS A CHARGE AGAINST POUCH OF "ASSAULT WITH A GUN."

AND HE'S OUT ON BOND AT THAT!

OH, THEY FACE OTHER MINOR CHARGES LIKE SQUATTING ON CITY PROPERTY—BUT I THINK WE HAVE A BIG SURPRISE UP OUR SLEEVE—EH, SAM?

A SURPRISE FOR THEM?

YOU CAN BET YOUR LAST, LITTLE OLD BOTTOM DOLLAR, KIDDO, IT'S FOR THEM!

"BUT RIGHT NOW SAM AND I ARE GOING OUT THERE AND TEAR THAT UNDERGROUND MOLE HOLE APART."

MEANWHILE Moved To Their New Apartment—

MOLENE, YOU'VE GOT TO PUT THESE SPARKLERS IN A SAFE PLACE.

NOW, GRANDPA MOLE—

GIVE ME TIME AND JUST BE THANKFUL EVERYTHING WORKED OUT SO WELL.

AND WHAT ABOUT THE DEMOLITION BOMB, MOLENE? IT NEVER WENT OFF.

I WONDER IF THE TIMING DEVICE WENT WRONG?

YOU'LL NEED THE HOMICIDE LIGHT.

RIGHT, SAM, AND THE ENTRANCE IS OVER THIS WAY.

CHESTER GOULD

SAM! ARE YOU OKAY?

CHESTER GOULD

I THINK THAT CURED MY HICCOUGHS.

174

CARRYING A CONCEALED WEAPON IS SERIOUS ENOUGH, POUCH, LET ALONE USING IT TO THREATEN A POLICE OFFICER.

BUT, YOUR HONOR, THEY WERE IN PLAIN CLOTHES. MY CLIENT THOUGHT THEY WERE ROBBERS!

YOUR HONOR, I SHOWED POUCH MY BADGE.

MR. POUCH WHAT IS ALL THIS?

I WEIGHED 500 POUNDS ONCE. I REDUCED TO 150. MY SKIN NEVER SHRANK.

I CARRY VARIOUS THINGS IN HERE CIGARS, KEYS, MONEY, ANYTHING.

BUT WHY WERE YOU CARRYING THIS IN THERE?

I'VE BEEN STUCK-UP TWICE. I WORK HARD FOR MY MONEY.

SINCE IT'S YOUR FIRST OFFENSE—YOU HAVE NO RECORD. I'M FINING YOU $200.

NEXT CASE.

MEANWHILE, AT THE ERST-WHILE PARK HIDEOUT OF MOLENE AND MOLE.

DESTRUCTION APPEARS TO BE TOTAL.

LUCKY IT WASN'T TOTAL FOR US, SAM.

SOMEBODY WAS DETERMINED TO ELIMINATE ALL EVIDENCE.

WHAT TH-?

AREA 7

THAT, GENTLEMEN, IS A CAP CRIMPER—FOR CUTTING FUSES AND CRIMPING BLASTING CAPS.

BLASTED INTO THE TREE?

YES, AND WOULDN'T THAT HAVE LOOKED NICE IN THE SIDE OF SOMEBODY'S HEAD?

WE'RE JUST LUCKY, SAM.

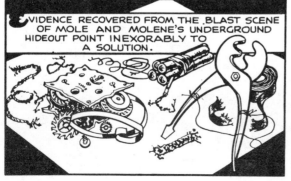

EVIDENCE RECOVERED FROM THE BLAST SCENE OF MOLE AND MOLENE'S UNDERGROUND HIDEOUT POINT INEXORABLY TO A SOLUTION.

THIS IS A PROFESSIONAL GADGET! CAP-CRIMPERS AND FUSE CUTTERS ARE NOT EVERYDAY KITCHEN TOOLS.

AND THEIR POSSESSION, WITHOUT AN EXPLOSIVE LICENSE, SHOULD BE SUSPICIOUS.

"AFTER SERVING A 19 YEAR PENITENTIARY SENTENCE, MOLE, I JUST CAN'T BELIEVE YOU'D INVOLVE YOURSELF IN THIS DIAMOND BUSINESS."

"YOU'RE RIGHT, MR. TRACY. I WENT ALONG WITH IT ONLY TO PROTECT MY GRANDDAUGHTER."

THE DIAMOND FILE AND IDENTIFICATION BUREAU HAVE IDENTIFIED 30 OF MOLENE'S COLLECTION AS STOLEN.

DID SHE MAKE THE TIME BOMB THAT BLEW UP YOUR UNDERGROUND HIDEOUT, MOLE?

NO. SHE MERELY STARTED THE CLOCK WHEN WE LEFT THE PLACE—SHE DID **NOT** MAKE THE BOMB.

SHE AND POUCH WORK FOR AN OUTFIT. ONE OF THEIR MEN PUT IN THE EXPLOSIVE SYSTEM WEEKS AGO.

WELL, MOLENE AND POUCH HAVE JUMPED BOND AND FLED. THEY'RE IN FOR **BIG** TROUBLE.

AFTER 19 YEARS IN PRISON, I RETURN TO THIS!

AND IN A CHEAP HONKY-TONK PUB.

I DON'T DRINK, MOLENE, AND REMEMBER, WE'RE FUGITIVES!

JUS' ONE MORE LI'L SIP.

SKOAL—

OUT!

SHE'S HAD IT! GET OUT!

I KNEW THIS WOULD HAPPEN.

SO!! I'VE BEEN LOOKING FOR YOU TWO.

GET IN HERE QUICK!

WHO ARE YOU?

IF I HADN'T PICKED YOU TWO UP WHEN YOU CAME OUT OF THAT DIRTY PUB—YOUR VALUE TO ME WOULD HAVE BEEN OVER.

NOW RELAX WHILE I POP SOME FRESH POPCORN.

"YOU HAVE YOUR OWN POPCORN MACHINE, JONNY?"

YEAH—BUT DON'T CHANGE THE SUBJECT—WHAT'S BUGGING YOU TWO?

"I—I CAN'T STAND MY GRANDFATHER AND HIS UNDERGROUND PHOBIA."

WELL, YOU'RE RID OF HIM. HE'S DISAPPEARED.

YOU TWO ARE THE BEST TEAM I'VE EVER HAD—BUT—WHAT HAS HAPPENED?

I CAN'T STAND WORKING WITH A WOMAN.

AND I CAN'T STAND WORKING WITH HIM.

NOW CUT THAT OUT! NO FAMILY QUARRELS.

WE GET ALONG IN THIS OUTFIT OR WE GET "REMOVED." IS THAT CLEAR?

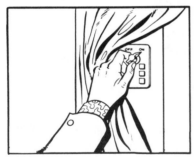

NOW RELAX. IT'S TUNED IN ON THE POLICE TV NETWORK. SHALL WE WATCH?

OH—WHY THAT'S GRANDPA!

HE'S TURNED STOOLIE!

IT WON'T PICK UP THEIR 2-WAY WRIST TV STUFF, BUT IT GETS THEIR CENTRAL STATION TELECASTS TO THE DISTRICTS.

MY GRAND-DAUGHTER OR NOT, SHE'S A CROOK! —AND I'LL TELL YOU HOW THEY WORK.

I'M OPPOSED TO VIOLENCE EXCEPT IN THIS CASE, —AND I'LL KILL THAT HUMPED-BACK OLD BUZZARD!

THE DIRTY STOOLIE.

WATCH YOUR LANGUAGE.

YOUR DAYS ARE OVER, MOLE—YOU'RE AN OLD MAN—BUT THANKS FOR THE INFORMATION ON THE DIAMOND APPARATUS.

YOU HAVE MONEY—WHY NOT GET YOURSELF INTO A REST HOME? RELAX.

I DON'T CARE WHAT HAPPENS TO ME BUT—MY GRANDDAUGHTER, MOLENE!

I FEAR THERE WILL BE FIRE AND BRIMSTONE APLENTY BEFORE MOLENE AND POUCH ARE BROUGHT TO HEEL.

IN THE APARTMENT OF JONNY SCORN. I'M INTERNATIONAL. I HAVE CONTACTS. I HAVE INFLUENCE.

I'LL OPEN BANK ACCOUNTS FOR YOU IN SWITZERLAND. YOU'LL BE TAKEN CARE OF.

MY DIAMONDS ARE FLOWN TO EUROPE IN 200 CARAT LOTS BY SPECIAL MESSENGER. NEVER PEDDLED HERE.

SPECIAL MESSENGER?

THROW BACK YOUR HEAD, POUCH, I WANT TO SEE YOUR CAPACITY.

AHA! NOT BAD! APPROXIMATELY 200 CARATS.

DO YOU THINK YOU COULD TRAVEL WITH $200,000 WORTH OF ROCKS IN YOUR "VALISE"?

TRAVEL?

WHERE?

TO SWITZERLAND?

ME?

WITH THIS 200-CARAT DIAMOND CARGO?

YOU'LL MAKE AN IDEAL MESSENGER, POUCH, AFTER YOU'VE BEEN PROPERLY DRESSED.

H'M?

181

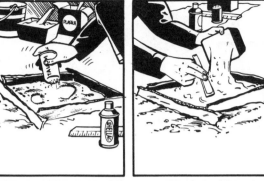

THEN THERE IS NO WAY WE CAN ESTABLISH OWNERSHIP OF THE CAP CRIMPER AND FUSE CUTTER WITHOUT FINGERPRINTS.

CORRECT! THE FACT THAT IT WAS BLASTED INTO A TREE PROVES NOTHING.

THESE NORMALLY ARE NOT OBTAINABLE BY CIVILIANS, EXCEPT WHERE DYNAMITE IS LICENSED TO BE SOLD.

AND THE LEGAL BUYERS OF DYNAMITE WOULD BE—

ROAD BUILDERS, CONTRACTORS, STONE QUARRY OPERATORS.

GUESS YOU SAW THE CASTS WE GOT OF A MAN'S AND A WOMAN'S FOOTPRINTS.

IT'S OUR IDEA, TRACY, THAT ONE OF THOSE TWO PERSONS OWNED THE CAP-CRIMPER.

AND IN THE APARTMENT OF JONNY SCORN.

BUT I DON'T LIKE THIS SEAL.

MY SWISS AGENT WILL DEAL WITH NO ONE UNLESS THE MERCHANDISE IS UNDER LOCK AND KEY.

BY USING THE EYELETS IN THE PLASTIC SNAPS, YOU SHOULD HAVE NO DISCOMFORT.

NOW, I MUST BE AWAY ABOUT AN HOUR. REMEMBER, POUCH, YOU LEAVE FOR THE AIRPORT AT FIVE.

I HAVE TO ATTEND A MEETING OF THE BOARD OF DIRECTORS OF MY STONE QUARRY.

STONE QUARRY?

YES, JONNY HANDLES BOTH KINDS OF ROCKS.

"MR. TRACY, I'M JOE YPPAH, PROPRIETOR OF 'JOE'S PLACE' ON 23RD ST."

"I HAD TO EVICT AN INTOXICATED WOMAN AND HER ESCORT A FEW WEEKS AGO, AND TO MY SURPRISE—"

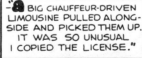

"—A BIG CHAUFFEUR-DRIVEN LIMOUSINE PULLED ALONG-SIDE AND PICKED THEM UP. IT WAS SO UNUSUAL I COPIED THE LICENSE."

"I TRIED TO LAUGH IT OFF, BUT THE MORE I THOUGHT ABOUT IT—"

JS2001

THIS EXPLAINS WHY MOLENE'S BOSS HAS ACCESS TO BLASTING MATERIAL.

SOME QUARRY!

NO TRUCKS NO TRAFFIC! LOOKS DESERTED.

SO HE OWNS THIS ROCK PILE, EH?

HOW DID YOU LEARN THE MAN'S IDENTITY, TRACY?

"THE BARTENDER THAT EJECTED MOLE AND POUCH FROM HIS PLACE NOTED THE LICENSE NUMBER OF THE LIMOUSINE THAT PICKED THEM UP."

JOE'S PLACE

—AND REPORTED IT TO POLICE PURELY ON A HUNCH.

COULD THIS BE JONNY SCORN'S FRONT FOR OTHER OPERATIONS?

OUR FILES REVEAL NO RECORD UNDER THAT NAME.

ELSEWHERE

I'M BACK.

ENJOY YOUR TRIP, POUCH?

NO! I HAD A CLOSE CALL.

THE JUDGE THAT FINED ME ON THE CONCEALED WEAPONS CHARGE WAS ON THE SAME PLANE.

THE SEAL

LUCKILY HE DIDN'T SEE ME! I'M THROUGH!

I QUIT.

EASY, POUCH! HOW ELSE COULD YOU MAKE A GRAND JUST BY TAKING A PLANE RIDE?

HAVE SOME FRESH POPCORN, POUCH.

CHESTER GOULD

THOSE DIAMONDS SCRATCHED MY POUCH! NO MORE TRIPS TO SWITZERLAND! I QUIT!

BUT—

MONEY DOESN'T HURT.

SNAP

CHESTER GOULD

POUCH, I LIKE YOU.

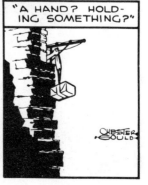

AERIAL VIEWS OF SCORN'S QUARRY PROVE ONE THING, CHIEF.

WHAT?

STONE IS NOT BEING TAKEN FROM THAT QUARRY. IT'S OUT OF OPERATION.

YOU'RE KIDDING.

NO, BUT A FEW ITEMS DID TURN UP.

FOR INSTANCE—FAINT TIRE MARKS CAN BE SEEN GOING DOWN INTO THE QUARRY.

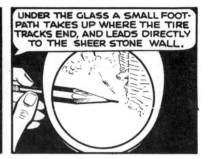

UNDER THE GLASS A SMALL FOOT-PATH TAKES UP WHERE THE TIRE TRACKS END, AND LEADS DIRECTLY TO THE SHEER STONE WALL.

LOVERS LANE! WHAT ELSE? HAVE YOU FORGOTTEN SO SOON, TRACY?

BUT, CHIEF, HAVE YOU FORGOTTEN THE WAYS OF CRIMINALS?

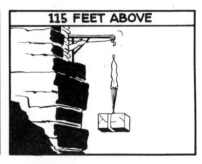

115 FEET ABOVE

YOU'VE JUDGED STERLING SILVER FOR YEARS, EH, MOLENE?

STERLING SILVER? —I SHOULD SAY I HAVE.

WAIT TILL YOU SEE THIS.

BEAUTIFUL. BEAUTIFUL! OLD WORLD HAND-CRAFTED PIECES.

I'VE GOT A WHOLE CAVE OF 'EM.

STERLING SILVER BY PARACHUTE!

WHO DROPPED IT?

WHO KNOWS?

"THIS WAY THE PROCURER NEVER SEES ME. I PAY LATER BY MESSENGER."

DYNAMITE + DIAMONDS + STERLING

YES IT APPEARS JONNY SCORN IS WELL DIVERSIFIED!

THERE'S NOTHING MORE FORLORN LOOKING THAN AN ABANDONED QUARRY.

IT'S GOT TO BE A FRONT FOR SOMETHING.

AND ITS OWNERSHIP WOULD GIVE SCORN THE RIGHT TO LEGALLY POSSESS DYNAMITE.

LET'S ROAM AROUND, BOYS. THE CHIEF SAYS THIS IS JUST A LOVERS LANE.

YEAH? WHERE ARE THE BEER CANS AND CIGARETTE BUTTS?

RIGHT! THERE ARE NONE.

WHAT A SPOT FOR TARGET PRACTICE!

GROOVY, SAM, LOOK!

JUST LIKE THE FBI!

THE REASON IT DIDN'T SHOW FROM THE AIR —IS, THE STONE OVERHANG.

CHESTER GOULD

What the DETECTIVES HAVE NOT DISCOVERED IS THAT THE "FIGURE" ON TARGET 4 IS MADE OF BLACK GAUZE AND IS EASILY SEEN THROUGH FROM THE REAR!

SCORN IS NOT AMONG THEM. HE WAS TO MEET ME HERE. I WONDER WHO THEY ARE?

CHESTER GOULD

LET'S SEE WHAT'S BACK OF HIS TARGET RANGE.

DO YOU FELLOWS SMELL CIGAR SMOKE?

ALL I SMELL IS SAM'S CIGARETTE.

189

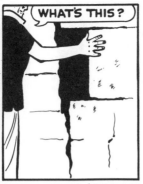

YES, EVEN IN POLICE WORK, OCCASIONALLY A PIECE OF GOOD LUCK TURNS UP!

IN A HIDDEN SPOT IN THE QUARRY UNDER A STONE LEDGE, SEAT HEIGHT, LAY THESE ARTICLES AS THOUGH 2 PEOPLE HAD PICNICKED.

CARDS IDENTIFY THE PURSE AS MOLENE'S.

AND IN THE PURSE THIS SERVING SPOON OF STERLING SILVER.

STERLING? ONE SPOON?

"THIS IS BIG TROUBLE, CHIEF, SCORN MAINTAINS AN FBI TYPE TARGET RANGE IN HIS QUARRY AND THERE'S PLENTY WE DIDN'T SEE."

"WE'RE GOING TO RETURN MOLENE'S BAG TO HER BY WAY OF PICKING HER UP FOR QUESTIONING."

DON'T GET EXCITED. I'LL GO QUIETLY.

"LIZZ IS OUT NOW TO BRING HER IN," SAYS TRACY.

--BUT NOT FAR! I'M SICK AND TIRED OF BEING HARASSED.

BY A DUMB BUNNY COP WHOSE ONLY ASSET IS TOO MUCH MASCARA

A QUICK TURN TO THE LEFT BY LIZZ.

FREEZING MOLENE'S WEAPON-ARM IN ONE QUICK FOLLOW THROUGH--

--LIZZ THROWS HER RIGHT LEG BEHIND MOLENE'S AND--THE SKIRMISH IS OVER!

GUESS I DO WEAR TOO MUCH MASCARA--BUT-- ON YOUR FEET, BABY--LET'S MARCH!

POLICE! HELP, HELP--

POLICE! POLICE

I'M A POLICE OFFICER! SHE PULLED THIS GUN ON ME.

POLICE!

I DON'T KNOW WHO YOU ARE, BUT NOBODY CAN BULLY A HELPLESS LITTLE LADY WHILE I'M AROUND.

WHEN I DISARMED HER AND THREW HER TO THE HOTEL FLOOR, SHE SET UP A HYSTERICAL YELL FOR POLICE.

NATURALLY, THE NEAREST MALE GUEST, THINKING I WAS THE ATTACKER, LET ME HAVE IT WITH HIS BRIEF CASE.

EVEN THOUGH I REPEATEDLY ANNOUNCED I WAS A POLICEWOMAN AND SHOWED MY BADGE.

I AM SORRY AND EMBARRASSED.

IT WAS AN IMPULSE I COULDN'T CONTROL.

IN THAT SPLIT SECOND, CHIEF, MOLENE GOT AWAY.

JUST THE SIGHT OF AN INNOCENT LITTLE GIRL LYING THERE PLEADING FOR HELP—

WHERE IS TRACY?

HE AND SAM ARE AT THE QUARRY.

MEANWHILE, THE FUGITIVE, MOLENE, ALSO HAS GONE TO THE QUARRY.

JONNY! THANK GOODNESS YOU'RE HERE! I-I--

MOLENE!

DYNAMITE

WHO IS SHE?

DYNAMITE

YNAMITE

AND TOPSIDE IN ONE OF THE ABANDONED SHACKS.

CHESTER GOULD

COULDN'T HAVE WORKED OUT BETTER—THEY'RE ALL THERE BUT POUCH.

SAY WHEN.

SO!

I FIND YOU DOWN HERE WITH ANOTHER WOMAN!

CHESTER GOULD

Sterling

SO, JONNY. YOUR MAIN INTEREST IS — ROMANCE, EH?

ROMANCE?

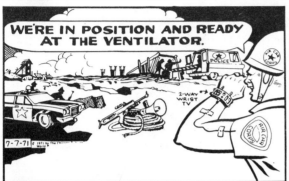

SHALL WE LOCK 'EM UP, TRACY?

OKAY! WE'VE TAKEN THEIR PICTURES AND TAPED THEIR VOICES—NOW, SAM, PUSH THE BUTTON.

SOMEBODY BLASTED US! THE DOOR WON'T OPEN.

THIS IS THE POLICE. YOU'RE BEING WATCHED BY TELEVISION. YOU'VE BEEN PHOTOGRAPHED.

YOUR ONLY EXIT NOW IS THROUGH THE OVERHEAD AIR SHAFT.

A ROPE LADDER IS BEING LOWERED. AS EACH OF YOU COME UP, STRETCH OUT, FACE DOWN.

WHO ARE YOU KIDDING, COPPERS?

OKAY, SCORN, THINK IT OVER. WE CAN WAIT AS LONG AS YOU CAN.

AND UNNOTICED, MOLENE REACHES! WHAT CAN SHE DO WITH A HAND GRENADE IN A DYNAMITE CACHE?

SEALED IN !

BETTER ORDER YOUR COFFIN, TRACY, BECAUSE WHEN I GET OUT—

AND IN THE EXCITEMENT, LOOK WHAT MOLENE SWIPED FROM EL TIGRESS' BELT.

JUST WHOSE SIDE IS MOLENE ON?

195

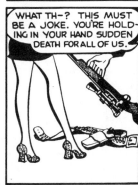

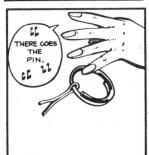

196

SCENE: THE UNDERGROUND QUARRY VAULT OF JONNY SCORN.

AND JONNY SCORN TAKES A POWDER VIA. HIS EMERGENCY VEHICLE.

A HISSING OF COMPRESSED AIR AS JONNY DEPARTS.

AND NONE TOO SOON, AS THE TOSSED GRENADE TOUCHES OFF A GIGANTIC BLAST.

—ABOVE GROUND, COMPLETE HAVOC!

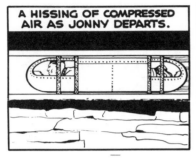

TRACY AND SAM, EMERGING FROM THE "CONTROL ROOM" SEVERAL HUNDRED FEET AWAY, ARE STAGGERED.

FIRST, THE SURFACE IS LIFTED, THEN DROPPED BACK.

EVERYBODY OKAY?

YES, TRACY, BUT WE FIGURE THE SAME CAN'T BE SAID OF MR. SCORN AND COMPANY!

SCENE: A CEMETERY ½ MILE AWAY.

"THEN NOBODY GOT OUT, EH?" ASKS TRACY.

I CALLED YOU OUT HERE, LIZZ, TO SEE IF YOU COULD IDENTIFY THIS.

IT WAS FOUND HANGING ON THIS TWIG AFTER THE EXPLOSION.

I'LL NEVER FORGET IT.

—HER VEIL AND ONE OF HER COMBS.

ALL THAT'S LEFT OF MOLENE.

"OBVIOUSLY 3 PEOPLE WERE DE-STROYED—SCORN AND MOLENE AND THE FEMALE REVOLUTIONIST."

ALAS, TRACY, YOUR APPRAISAL OF THE CASUALTIES IS SLIGHTLY EXAGGERATED.

SCORN, THANKS TO HIS COMPRESSED AIR ESCAPE SYSTEM, SITS IN HIS APARTMENT EAVESDROPPING.

HE WAS DEALING IN EXPLOSIVES VERY, VERY BIG.

WHAT SET IT OFF?

UNFORTUNATELY HE SHOT UP OUR TV CAMERA BEFORE THE BLAST AND WE COULD NOT SEE.

BUT WE KNOW THEIR ONLY CHANCE OF ESCAPE WAS THE ROPE LADDER WE WERE LETTING DOWN THROUGH THE OLD AIR VENT, SO—

BUT THERE WAS ANOTHER ESCAPE ROUTE, YES, INDEED!

THOSE PUFFS OF DUST AND SMOKE— WILL THEY REVEAL SCORN'S SECRET?

SMOKE COMING OUT OF A MAUSOLEUM!

"AT HI-OAKS CEMETERY —THE SIDE ON ARCHER AVENUE."

HI-OAKS CEMETERY? IT ADJOINS THIS QUARRY.

BLAST NUMBER TWO? OBVIOUSLY IT WAS SCORN'S SECRET ESCAPE SYSTEM WHICH, APPARENTLY, HE WAS UNABLE TO USE. YOU SEE, THERE'S NO MACHINERY AT THIS END.

IT MUST ALL BE BACK IN THE QUARRY. HEAT FROM THE MAIN BLAST, IN A DELAYED ACTION, SET OFF BLASTING CAPS THAT SET OFF UNEXPLODED DYNAMITE!

THEN THE TALLY IS THREE DEAD—SCORN TOO? —OR IS HE?

IN ANSWER TO TRACY'S QUESTION— COUNTERFEIT, AND YOU KNEW IT!

THAT'S THE WAY YOU PAID ME OFF FOR THAT LAST COLLECTING JOB, WITH COUNTERFEIT!

POUCH, OLD BUDDY, I MUST HAVE PEELED THAT OFF THE WRONG ROLL. YOU CHEATED ME!

HERE, I'M SORRY, OLD PAL. YOU'RE BAD NEWS TO ME, SCORN. F'INSTANCE I'D HAVE BEEN BLOWN TO BITS IN YOUR QUARRY IF I HADN'T BEEN LATE.

TAKE THIS THOUSAND WHILE I GET YOU SOME POPCORN. I'LL GET IT MYSELF!

WHILE POUCH SCOOPS UP POPCORN, HE DEPOSITS SOME SMALL OBJECTS IN THE UNHEATED POPPING PAN—

THOSE SIX OBJECTS? SIX BLASTING CAPS!

SO, BELIEVING SCORN DEAD— OUR NEXT MOVE IS TO SEARCH HIS PENTHOUSE. GOSH! I'D LIKE TO GO ALONG.

OCCASIONALLY, POUCH, A COUNTERFEIT BILL WILL GET MIXED IN—

BUT NEVER WOULD I KNOWINGLY SLIP ONE TO YOU, OLD PAL. I'M SORRY.

LET'S SEAL OUR FRIENDSHIP WITH A BAG OF FRESH POPCORN, EH? NO, THANKS, GOTTA GO, SCORN.

POPCORN AND BLASTING CAPS! SCORN DOESN'T KNOW THE CAPS ARE THERE, BUT POUCH DOES!

POPCORN AND BLASTING CAPS!

SCORN, UNAWARE OF IMPENDING DANGER, SITS SMUGLY ENJOYING NEWS STORIES OF HIS QUARRY DEBACLE.

COLUMNS ABOUT MY QUARRY "DEATH!" THEY THINK I'M DEAD! HA, HA, HA!

AH, HA, HA, HA! THE DUMMIES THINK I'M DEAD!

BELIEVING SCORN DEAD, AND HOPING TO UNCOVER INFORMATION THAT WILL CLEAR UP HIS INTERNATIONAL CRIME AND CREW HEAD FOR JONNY SCORN'S PENTHOUSE.

WHAT WAS THAT?

YOU'RE IN HOODLUM COUNTRY NOW, PODNER.

IN THE **PENTHOUSE**? THAT'S SCORN'S DIGGIN'S.

YEAH, MR. TRACY, AND A PENTHOUSE FIRE IS ALWAYS ROUGH.

"WHAT **GIVES NOW?** SAYS SAM.

"I SMELL GASOLINE FUMES," SAYS LIZZ

IS THAT A POPCORN MACHINE?

THEN HE DID ESCAPE THE QUARRY DEBACLE.

ONLY TO BE TRAPPED IN HIS OWN PENTHOUSE.

BUT IS IT SCORN?

THE BLAST AND THE FIRE? IS THIS A SUICIDE?" ASKS SAM. "NOT IF I KNOW JONNY SCORN'S TYPE, IT ISN'T." SAYS TRACY.

LOOKS LIKE IT CENTERED IN THE POPCORN MACHINE.

I GUESS WHEN JONNY SCORN WANTED POPCORN, HE DIDN'T MESS AROUND.

IT'S STILL POPPING!

15 lb. POP CORN

WAS THAT GASOLINE BURNER THE CAUSE?

NOT A CHANCE! **EXPLOSIVE** DID THIS.

APPARENTLY SCORN ESCAPED THE BIG EXPLOSION ONLY TO BECOME VICTIM OF A SMALLER ONE.

AND IN HIS OWN PENTHOUSE!

JUST HOW DO YOU EXPLAIN SCORN'S DEATH, TRACY?

THAT, LIZZ, WILL TAKE A LITTLE STUDY.

BUT METAL FRAGMENTS INDICATE AN EXPLOSION THAT CENTERED IN THE POPCORN MACHINE.

"AND ITS OLD-TIME GASOLINE FUEL SYSTEM WOULD ACCOUNT FOR THE FIRE."

AN EXPENSIVE INSTALLATION JUST TO INTERCEPT POLICE BULLETINS.

HE MUST HAVE KNOWN OUR EVERY MOVE.

"YES, AND WHO COULD HAVE OUTSMARTED SCORN LIKE THIS?"

WHO?

TCH, TCH, POOR FELLOW.

BUT—ALL OF MY TRUE FRIENDS—THEY'RE GONE, TOO. I'M ALONE.

CHESTER GOULD

NOTHING LEFT TO CHEER ME—BUT THE COMIC STRIPS.

SCORN   MOLENE   EL TIGRESS   MOLE

DECEASED

THREE GONE, AND THE MOLE RETIRED FROM THE CRIME SCENE.

AND POUCH, WITHOUT A LEADER, LIVES IN A WORLD OF STUPID HARMLESSNESS.

"AND SO—ANOTHER CASE IS—"

CLOSED

A DIAMOND'S "FINGERPRINT."

CLOSED, DID HE SAY?

ANOTHER PASS, PILOT, —BUT A LITTLE LOWER, PLEASE.

SCENE: THE QUARRY SITE OF THE EXPLOSION INVOLVING THE LATE JONNY SCORN'S ILLICIT DYNAMITE CACHE.

"PARDON ME, SIR, I'M JUST A COMMERCIAL PILOT, BUT I AM CURIOUS AS TO WHAT THAT WAS ALL ABOUT."

I HAVE A GRAND-DAUGHTER BURIED UNDER 40 MILLION TONS OF ROCK THERE.

POOR MOLENE!

THE CLONING OF MUMBLES

PRINCIPAL PERPETRATORS: **Mumbles (?);**
Dr. Zy Ghote; Roundy

ORIGINALLY APPEARED: April 3, 1979–July 23, 1979
WRITER: Max Allan Collins   ARTIST: Rick Fletcher

When I took over as the writer of "Dick Tracy," I was told by editor Don Michel and publisher Bob Reed that I ought to try to do a story about a classic "Tracy" villain at least once a year—for a while, anyway.

And for a while, anyway, I did: only (as I mentioned earlier) Chester Gould was ruthless about bumping off his great bad guys. Some of them were so irrevocably dead that using them became out of the question. (In order to write about Flattop and Shaky, I wound up doing a flashback story, to the war years, in 1985; it was collected in book form as *Tracy's Wartime Adventures,* Ken Pierce Books, 1986.)

So I began looking for loopholes in Gould's continuity; I tried to see if there were at least one or two of the greatest grotesques that might somehow be brought back to life.

Gould himself had done this with Mumbles—seemingly killing him in forty-seven, resurrecting him in fifty-five; and it seemed fitting, and a little funny, for me to do the same with that much-loved character, whose mush-mouthed diction somehow takes the edge off his murderous behavior. A "Tracy" tradition is to push science to near science-fiction limits, and doing a story about a clone seemed a fun, topical way to bring the familiar face of a fiendish foe back into Tracy's life.

My late partner, Rick Fletcher—who had been Chet Gould's final assistant—did a terrific job on this, our fifth story together; his work here is typically crisp and modern, a nice marriage of his more naturally realistic style and Gould's cartoonier one.

Incidentally, at the beginning of the story Tracy has gone to the West Coast, where he had sent his wife, Tess, to get her out of the line of fire during the previous, perilous continuity (*Big Boy's Open Contract,* reprinted in *The Dick Tracy Casebook*, St. Martin's, 1990).

THE **COMPUTER CRIME WAVE** MAY BE JUST BEGINNING, DIET...

"AS COMPUTERS TAKE OVER SOCIETY'S BASIC FUNCTIONS, WILL WE SOON BE AT THE MERCY OF THIEVES AND EXTORTIONISTS?"

I'M CONVINCED. CARE TO TRY CONVINCING A **TV** AUDIENCE?

WHAT?

YOU'RE AN ELOQUENT SPOKESMAN ON THE COMPUTER CRIME PROBLEM...

SO I WANT YOU TO APPEAR WITH ME, ON A TALK SHOW ON THAT SUBJECT.

DON'T KNOW WHY I COULDN'T...

GOOD. GRAB YOUR TOOTHBRUSH— THEY TAPE THE SHOW IN CALIFORNIA.

CHIEF, I **KNOW** WHAT DIET'S UP TO.

"THIS TALK SHOW APPEARANCE IN CALIFORNIA IS HIS WAY OF GETTING ME OUT THERE TO SEE TESS."

VALLEY of the CLIFFHANGERS

NEVER MIND DIET'S MOTIVES— JUST GO **DO IT!** IT'S GOOD PUBLIC RELATIONS! AND GIVE MY LOVE TO TESS.

208

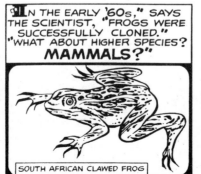

CAN ANIMALS BE CLONED? ASK THESE CLONED MICE—

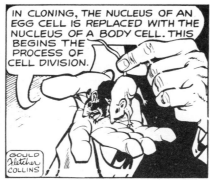

IN CLONING, THE NUCLEUS OF AN EGG CELL IS REPLACED WITH THE NUCLEUS OF A BODY CELL. THIS BEGINS THE PROCESS OF CELL DIVISION.

THE OFFSPRING PRODUCED IS AN **EXACT DUPLICATE** OF ITS "FATHER"—WHO COULD BE MALE **OR** FEMALE.

CLONING A MAN **WAS** A CHALLENGE.

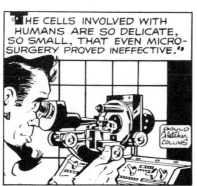

THE CELLS INVOLVED WITH HUMANS ARE SO DELICATE, SO SMALL, THAT EVEN MICRO-SURGERY PROVED INEFFECTIVE."

BUT I FOUND A WAY AROUND THAT," SAYS DR. ZY GHOTE.

YOU'RE ON IN ONE MINUTE, MUMBLES.

EXCUSE ME, DOCTOR—BUT SHORTLY AFTER YOUR NOBEL PRIZE IN GENETICS, WEREN'T YOU AND SOME OF YOUR WORK **DISCREDITED?**

I **WAS** OVERZEALOUS—AND PAID THE PRICE. I WORKED IN **EXILE**, FOR 25 YEARS.

AS A RESULT, I WAS **20** YEARS AHEAD OF THE SCIENTIFIC COMMUNITY —AND **MY** CLONE IS NOT A BABY, **BUT A MAN!**"

YOU'RE ON, MUMBLES...

YES, AFTER MY NOBEL PRIZE, SOME OF MY WORK **WAS** DISCREDITED.

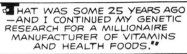

"HAT WAS SOME 25 YEARS AGO —AND I CONTINUED MY GENETIC RESEARCH FOR A MILLIONAIRE MANUFACTURER OF VITAMINS AND HEALTH FOODS."

GEORGE OZONE

In the WINGS— MUMBLES, YOU'RE ON **NEXT**—

WHTZ **TRAZY** DOIN HERE?

WHY WAIT **20 YEARS** TO UNVEIL THE FIRST HUMAN **CLONE**?

"WHEN GEORGE OZONE DIED, HIS ESTATE'S EXECUTORS **HALTED** MY RESEARCH — WITH THE CLONING EXPERIMENT IN PROGRESS."

GREEN MOVING COMPAN

FRAGILE

THEN, IN CANADA, LAST YEAR, I MET A YOUNG MAN— **PROOF** OF MY EXPERIMENT'S SUCCESS...

YOU **RECOGNIZED** THIS YOUNG CANADIAN?

HE WAS THE **IMAGE** OF THE "DONOR" IN MY CLONING EXPERIMENT. FROM A PICTURE HE SHOWED ME, I RECOGNIZED HIS LATE MOTHER AS THE RECIPIENT.

MY EXPERIMENT HAD BEEN FRUITFUL, AFTER ALL, AS YOU CAN SEE.

MUMBLES!

NOT MUMBLES, DETECTIVE TRACY—

MUMBLES IS **DEAD**— AND IF HE WERE ALIVE, HE'D BE **40-SOME** YEARS OF AGE. **THIS** YOUNG MAN— **MUMBLES TWO**— IS 20.

AND DESPITE YOUR CAUSING HIS "FATHER'S" DEATH, HE HOLDS NO GRUDGE.

NO RDGE.

THAT'S OUR SHOW FOR TODAY, FOLKS.

"MANY QUESTIONS WE DIDN'T HAVE TIME TO ASK ARE ANSWERED IN THIS NEW BOOK."

The CLONING OF MUMBLES by dr. zy ghote

YOU DON'T **BUY** ANY OF THIS, DO YOU, DIET?

I DON'T KNOW.

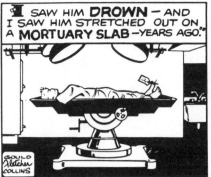

TRACY, THIS GUY **CAN'T** BE MUMBLES—MUMBLES IS **DEAD!**

SAM, YOU WEREN'T SITTING NEXT TO HIM ON THAT **TV** SHOW. IT WAS MUMBLES, ALL RIGHT.

"OR HIS **CLONE**," SAYS LIZZ.

ELSEWHERE

LONDON CALLING, SIR.

NEVER MIND LONDON— **GET DR. ZY GHOTE!**

LIZZ, DIG INTO THE **MUMBLES** FILE—CONCENTRATE ON HIS **"DEATH."**

"SAM, YOU AND I HAVE AN APPOINTMENT AT STATE UNIVERSITY." While—

CALSMI.

WHAT DID HE SAY?

HE WANTS ME TO CALL SMITH— BUT NO NEED: SMITH'LL CALL **US.**

WHAT DO YOU EXPECT LIZZ TO FIND?

"I DON'T KNOW—BUT SHE WASN'T INVOLVED IN THE PREVIOUS MUMBLES CASE, SO SHE'LL HAVE AN OPEN MIND."

HM-M—THIS MAY BE SOMETHING...

While ON THE WEST COAST—

I HAVE DR. GHOTE ON THE LINE, SIR.

GOOD!!!

At STATE UNIVERSITY...

5-3-79

...TRACY AND SAM MEET WITH THE CHAIRMAN OF THE BIOLOGY DEPARTMENT—

GENTLEMEN—AS TO THIS "CLONING" BUSINESS...

"I'M CONVINCED IT'S A **HOAX**."

WHILE

OF COURSE WE CAN GET TOGETHER, MR. SMITH —**EVENTUALLY.**

PROFESSOR LEARNED, HASN'T CLONING ALREADY BEEN ACCOMPLISHED?

"OF COURSE—WE'VE DONE IT **HERE**—WITH FROGS. HUMAN CLONING IS THEORETICALLY **POSSIBLE,** BUT DOUBTFUL AT THIS POINT."

"ZY GHOTE'S BOOK IS CLEARLY A **SHAM**," SAYS THE PROFESSOR.

WHY THE **DELAY,** DR. ZY GHOTE?

BABY FOOD

Panel 1:
SEVERAL UNRELATED FACTORS, WHEN TIED TOGETHER, ADD UP TO MUMBLES **CONNING** US INTO **THINKING** HE WAS DEAD...

Panel 2:
Elsewhere — DR. ZY GHOTE AND COMPANY PREPARE FOR THE NEXT STOP ON THEIR BOOK TOUR —

I WISH YOU WOULDN'T CARRY THAT THING.

SHU TUP!

THE CLONING OF MUMBLES dr zy ghote

GOULD FLETCHER COLLINS

Panel 3:
THE DROWNING OF MUMBLES, 20 YEARS AGO, OCCURRED **OUTSIDE OUR COUNTY.**

Panel 4:
THE AMBULANCE THAT PICKED UP HIS 'BODY' WAS PRIVATELY OWNED — FROM A LOCAL FUNERAL HOME."

RESTWELL FUNERAL HOME

Panel 5:
AND THE MORTUARY WHERE TRACY SAW HIM, BRIEFLY, WAS IN THAT OTHER COUNTY, TOO."

GOULD FLETCHER COLLINS

Panel 6:
I REMEMBER... A SHERIFF HIX WAS INVOLVED.

A GOOD MAN — RECENTLY RETIRED. YOU'RE NOT SUGGESTING...

PATTON

Panel 7:
I'M SUGGESTING NOTHING. BUT CONSIDER THIS STRAY FACT —

Panel 8:
MUMBLES WAS A STUDENT OF YOGA TECHNIQUES ...SOME OF WHICH CAN SIMULATE DEATH."

QUIZAYN WHAD DEE ZAY!

WHAT DID HE SAY?

HE SAID, STOP SAYING "WHAT DID HE SAY."

NOW—TAKE A LOOK AT THIS DEATH CERTIFICATE—NOTICE ANYTHING *UNUSUAL*?

THERE'S ONLY ONE SIGNATURE ON THIS DEATH CERTIFICATE—

RIGHT. IT'S THE CORONER'S SIGNATURE.

NOT UNUSUAL, IN SOME LOCALES.

"*Y*ES—COUNTY CORONER **RESTWELL**," SAYS LIZZ. "NAME SOUND FAMILIAR?"

GATIKS?

YES, I HAVE THE TICKETS, MUMBLES.

THE DEATH CERTIFICATE LACKS A DOCTOR'S SIGNATURE.

BUT IT'S NO PHONY—IT'S LEGAL.

CORONER IS AN ELECTIVE OFFICE—RESTWELL, A MORTICIAN, WAS QUALIFIED ENOUGH.

RESTWELL! THAT'S THE NAME OF THE FUNERAL HOME WHOSE AMBULANCE HAULED MUMBLES AWAY!

SNAP

MUMBLES WAS THE PROTEGE OF MILLIONAIRE HEALTH FADDIST GEORGE OZONE.

"*O*ZONE'S RESEARCH INTO MATTERS OF MIND AND BODY INCLUDED THE STUDY AND MASTERY OF CERTAIN YOGA TECHNIQUES."

GEORGE OZONE

SOME ADVANCED YOGA TECHNIQUES CAN EFFECTIVELY SIMULATE **DEATH!**

SO—MUMBLES WASN'T **DEAD**—HE WAS DOING YOGA!

HOW FAR-FETCHED CAN YOU GET?

"*O*H, I DON'T KNOW," SAYS TRACY. "MAYBE YOU PREFER BELIEVING MUMBLES HAS A **CLONE**?"

WHAZ HAPN?

WE'RE TAKING OFF—

220

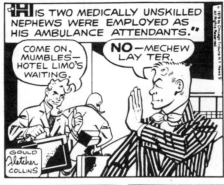

YOU SUSPECT CARVER, THE PLASTIC SURGEON, GAVE MUMBLES A FACELIFT, HUH?

TO MAKE HIM A "CLONE" OF HIMSELF, YES.

The CLONING of MUMBLES

AND THEN MUMBLES, TYPICALLY, SET OUT TO **KILL** CARVER," SAYS TRACY. "BUT UNTYPICALLY, **FAILED**... MAKING DR. CARVER A POTENTIAL WITNESS **AGAINST** HIM..."

GOULD/Fletcher/COLLINS

DR. GHOTE, MY FIRST— AND ONLY— MARRIAGE ENDED IN **TRAGEDY**...

MY WIFE, AFTER OUR DIVORCE, WAS EMPLOYED BY ME AS A RESEARCH SCIENTIST— UNBEKNOWNST TO ME, SHE PLOTTED AGAINST ME—EVENTUALLY SHE COMMITTED **SUICIDE**."

I NEVER REMARRIED.

PSST—THI SUCKERZ RIPE FER PLUCKIN.

I **HAD** A SON—**BRILLIANT.** A YOUNG GENIUS...

"HE INVENTED THE 2-WAY WRIST RADIO; HE WAS BLINDED DEVELOPING THE **ATOMIC LIGHT**... BUT HIS RESEARCH WENT ON."

THIEF TEMPORARILY BLINDED

2-WAY WRIST RADIO

TO ME, THE BOY REPRESENTED YOUTH SUCCEEDING IN SPITE OF HANDICAP— I MISS HIM.

GOULD Fletcher COLLINS

DIET'S STORY: "AFTER THE SUICIDE OF MY EX-WIFE, AND THE DEATH OF MY SON, I LOST MYSELF IN MY WORK— NEVER REMARRIED."

OUR LATEST INVENTION, THE 2-WAY WRIST TV.

1964

NOW, I'M GROWING OLDER —AND HAVE NO SON— **NO HEIR.**

GOULD Fletcher COLLINS

DR. ZY GHOTE, I NEED YOUR HELP.

THOUGHT YOU'D NEVER ASK...

A **CLONE** OF MYSELF, DR. GHOTE— COULD IT BE A SORT OF **SON** TO ME?

THE **IDEAL** HEIR— YOUR FLESH AND BLOOD, LITERALLY... YOUR PHYSICAL DUPLICATE, BUT AN INDIVIDUAL IN HIS OWN RIGHT.

GOULD Fletcher COLLINS

IT'S A **WONDERFUL** NOTION, DIET SMITH—I'M GLAD **YOU** THOUGHT OF IT...

WE'LL CONFIRM THE FINANCIAL ARRANGEMENTS SOON.

DIET SMITH ENTERPRISES

SAM TO LIZZ—I'VE JUST SEEN SOMETHING **WILD**—IS TRACY BACK YET?

"HE'S STILL AT THE HOSPITAL," SAYS LIZZ.

WE CAN TALK IN THE COFFEE SHOP, MRS. CARVER.

ALL RIGHT.

MRS. CARVER—HAS YOUR HUSBAND TAKEN ANY TRIPS THE LAST YEAR OR SO?

EITHER BUSINESS OR VACATION—WITH OR WITHOUT YOU.

JUST LAS VEGAS—WILL LIKES TO GAMBLE, AS YOU KNOW.

COFFEE SHOP

OH—AND SIX MONTHS AGO HE ATTENDED A CONVENTION—IN CANADA.

HM-MM...

THANK YOU, MRS. CARVER ...YOU'VE BEEN MOST HELPFUL.

"WHEN WILL IS WELL ENOUGH TO SPEAK TO YOU, I'M SURE HE'LL HELP, TOO," SAYS MRS. CARVER.

And at HQ—

DIET SMITH? SHAKING HANDS WITH GHOTE AND MUMBLES?

TRACY'LL **FLIP!**

DIET SMITH? MEETING WITH **GHOTE?**

2-WAY WRIST TV

AND "MUMBLES TWO"—WE'VE GOT VIDEO TAPE TO **PROVE** IT. SAM BROADCAST THE MEETING VIA 2-WAY WRIST TV.

VIDEO TAPE

"THEN I'M GOING TO SMITH'S **NOW**," TRACY SAYS, "AND GET TO THE BOTTOM OF THIS."

GIMME PAPER!

ER...OKAY, MUMBLES.

PLASTIC SURGERY

WHILE I'M SEEING DIET SMITH, CHECK WITH THE CANADIAN AUTHORITIES.

DIET SMITH ENTERPRISES

SEE IF THERE REALLY WAS A MEDICAL CONVENTION IN TORONTO LAST NOVEMBER.

"CARVER'S CANADIAN 'CONVENTION' MAY HAVE BEEN MUMBLES' **FACELIFT**."

THA ★!✲!✲★

WHAT DID HE SAY?

DAILY DAILY

PLASTIC SURGEON SURVIVES HIT-AND-RUN

DIET—I THINK I CAN GUESS WHY GHOTE'S WORK INTERESTS YOU.

I KNOW HOW HARD THE LOSS OF YOUR SON HIT YOU—IT LEFT A VOID IN YOUR LIFE...

BUT DON'T LET YOUR EMOTIONS LEAD YOU INTO BELIEVING THIS PHONY 'CLONING' HOAX!"

YOUR WORK, MUMBLES?

CLONING ISN'T A HOAX, TRACY—IT...

DIET— PLEASE!

CLONING MAY OR MAY NOT BE POSSIBLE—BUT THE MUMBLES CLONE IS A PHONY!

HIS 'DEATH,' 20 YEARS AGO, WAS FAKED—SO IS HIS 'YOUTH,' THANKS TO PLASTIC SURGERY."

YEH— I DIDIT.

CAN YOU SHOW ME PROOF THAT THE MUMBLES CLONE IS PHONY?

NO, WE'RE STILL GATHERING IT—

I THOUGHT SO.

"TRACY," SAYS DIET. "I'M AFRAID I'LL HAVE TO ASK YOU TO LEAVE—"

MUMBLES— I TOLD YOU NO VIOLENCE!

YOU TRIED TO KILL CARVER? RAN HIM DOWN?

WE'VE GOT BIG MONEY RIDING ON THIS, MUMBLES, AND YOU'RE BLOWING IT!

SHU TUP.

While—

DIET—I'M ONLY TRYING TO HELP.

GOODBYE, TRACY.

DON TELME WHA TODO!

WHAT DID HE SAY?

SHUT-UP!

While—

HOW'D YOUR TALK WITH DIET GO?

NEVER MIND THAT —THE HOSPITAL SAYS WE CAN TALK TO CARVER NOW!

ONLY THE D.A. CAN GUARANTEE YOU **IMMUNITY.**

I'M CALLING MY ATTORNEY!

FINE. LET US KNOW WHAT YOU WORK OUT.

"THEN WE CAN TALK AGAIN, ABOUT PUTTING THAT GUARD BACK ON YOUR DOOR..."

THIS'LL STOP **ALL** DOC CARV'S **PAIN...**

TAKE A LITERARY HOAX, LIKE THAT FAKE HOWARD HUGHES BOOK—

AFTER SOME MONTHS IN JAIL, A MAN MIGHT CONTINUE HIS **WORK,** WITH SUFFICIENT **FUNDING...**

So, IF YOU'RE INVOLVED WITH THE **REAL** MUMBLES, DR. GHOTE — GET OUT **NOW,** WHILE YOU CAN."

BUT?

DON BLAB!

ROUNDY—**WHERE'S** MUMBLES?

HE WENT OUT TO BUY SOME STUFF— DR. GHOTE, MUMBLES DIDN'T WANT ME TO SAY NOTHIN'...

"BUT I THINK HE'S PLANNIN' TO KILL THAT PLASTIC SURGEON, DR. CARVER—"

YOU SAW MUMBLES "FOOLING AROUND" WITH **THIS?**

HI BOYZ— WHAS NEW?

COME ON IN, MUMBLES — IT'S TIME **WE TALKED.**

ROUNDY TOLD ME ABOUT YOUR PLAN TO KILL CARVER—

MUMBLES, YOUR VIOLENCE HAS TO STOP!

UH-H-

MUMBLES WILL GO TO THE HOSPITAL AND KILL CARVER...

"...AND THERE'S **NO** WAY OF **STOPPING** HIM..."

MM-M-M-M♪♫

YOUR HUSBAND'S DOING WELL, MRS. CARVER. HE'LL BE OUT OF HERE **SOON.**

City Hospital
VISITORS PARKING

GOTTA FIND OUT CARV'S ROOM NUMMER...

DOCTOR'S SMOCK UNDER JACKET

WHAT A NICE IDEA, FRED—HAVING THE GIFT SHOP SEND FLOWERS UP TO MOM'S ROOM.

LOBBY

HOSPITAL gift Shop We DELIVER

EXCUSE ME, SIR—I CAN'T UNDERSTAND YOU—CAN YOU SPEAK MORE **CLEARLY?**

Gift Shop

SAID I WAN HAVE SOME **FLOWERS** D'LIVERED TO DOC TER CARVER'S **ROOM.**

Gift Shop

NUMBER OF CARVER'S ROOM OBTAINED FROM SWITCHBOARD

phone

HELLO, DOCTOR— DELIVERING SOME FLOWERS TO A PATIENT.

THAS NIZE.

HOPE YOU LIKE YOUR FLOWERS. DR. CARVER.

NO P'LICE GUARD —NO DOCS ROUND, ER NURZES...

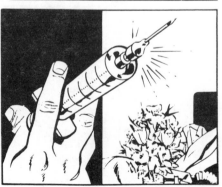

"DR." MUMBLES CALLS ON DR. CARVER...

HIYA, MUMBLES.

SOCK!

I'M SURPRISED AT YOU, MUMBLES. DIDN'T YOU KNOW PRACTICIN' MEDICINE WITHOUT A LICENSE IS ILLEGAL?

HOTEL MANAGER

DO NOT DISTURB

WELL, **DR. GHOTE**—LOOKS LIKE YOU AND MUMBLES MUST'VE HAD A FALLING OUT.

I WANT A LAWYER.

WOULDN'T YOU LIKE ME TO **UNTIE** YOU FIRST?

LIZZ TO TRACY—GHOTE AND HIS FLUNKY, "ROUNDY" WILLIS, IN CUSTODY—

2-WAY WRIST T V

GHOTE SAYS HE TRIED TO STOP MUMBLES—THAT HE WASN'T INVOLVED IN ANY **VIOLENCE.**

WHAT DID HE SAY?

HE SAID, TELL IT TO THE JUDGE.

WHA DID HE ZAY?

HE SAID YOU HAVE THE RIGHT TO REMAIN SILENT.

CARVER COOPERATED IN THE PLAN TO SWITCH PLACES WITH HIM, BUT HE STILL HASN'T AGREED TO TESTIFY AGAINST MUMBLES.

"WITHOUT CARVER, CAN WE PROVE THIS IS THE **REAL MUMBLES**?"

THIS GUY IS **MUMBLES**, ALL RIGHT— FINGERPRINTS MATCH.

"BUT SO WOULD HIS **CLONE'S**!" SAYS SAM. "WE GOT TO **PROVE** HE'S THE REAL McCOY, OR THERE GOES THE **FRAUD** CASE..."

UM-M UM-M

WE GOT HIM **COLD** ON ATTEMPTED **MURDER**—OF TRACY!

D.A. MAY CLAIM **ENTRAPMENT.**

EVEN **WITHOUT** CARVER'S TESTIMONY, WE CAN **PROVE** THE "CLONE" IS THE **REAL MUMBLES.**

PLASTIC SURGERY, EVEN AT ITS MOST SOPHISTICATED, LEAVES HIDDEN BUT IDENTIFIABLE **SCARS**—

FURTHERMORE—MUMBLES NEVER HAD A SPEECH IMPEDIMENT—MERELY SLOPPY SPEECH HABITS, WHICH **DON'T** DERIVE FROM **HEREDITY**!

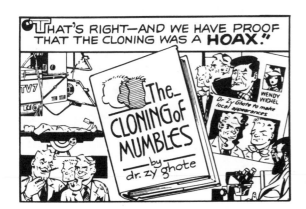

THE CRYONIC MAN

PRINCIPAL PERPETRATORS: **Pruneface;
Dr. Kryos Freezdrei**

*ORIGINALLY APPEARED: August 22, 1983–
December 24, 1983*
WRITER: Max Allan Collins   *ARTIST: Dick Locher*

The following tale is, in a way, a variation on the one you've just read. Where the cloning of Mumbles was a hoax, however, the thawing of Pruneface is something else again . . . .

In looking for loopholes in the deaths of Gould grotesques, what better escape clause could Chester Gould have provided me than to *freeze* a major villain? This opened the refrigerator door for us to do another science-oriented tale, focusing on cryogenics.

Tracy fan John Wells—in his article "Max Collins' 'Dick Tracy'—The Top Twelve" (*The Comics Buyers Guide*, November 30, 1990)—chose this story as the best post-Gould continuity thus far. Specifically, he said, "The first complete story by Collins and Locher remains their best." (Incidentally, Wells's second-place choice, *Dick Tracy at the Wax Museum*, is the final story in this collection.)

This was indeed the first complete story I did

with Dick Locher, former Gould assistant and Pulitzer Prize-winning editorial cartoonist. Dick had completed the previous story, begun by the late Rick Fletcher (whose dedication to the strip found him at his drawing board until he literally no longer could hold a brush). In fact, Dick had done most of that story—which was about a new, second-generation Crimestoppers Club—and was properly warmed up for this chiller.

I was delighted by Dick's portrayal of Pruneface, and the art in this story is suitably film-*noir*-ish, and yet displays the Locher touch for humor, so in keeping with the Gould tradition. Dick was assisted throughout by his talented young son John, whose tragic early death in 1986 remains Dick Tracy's saddest defeat. The father-and-son team's work on this story is a testimony to what might have been had fate been kinder.

VITAMIN WAS WONDERFUL TONIGHT, DICK!

WE'LL HAVE TO GO BACKSTAGE AND COMPLIMENT HIM—

"DICK, ISN'T THIS THE FIRST MUSICAL HE'S EVER PRESENTED AT HIS DINNER THEATER?"

"'YES,' TRACY SAYS. 'HE MUST BE VERY PLEASED RIGHT ABOUT NOW.'"

WOE—OH WOE IS ME...

I'M SURE VITAMIN WILL BE TICKLED TO SEE US—

KNOCK KNOCK

AH, RICHARD-TESS, M'DEAR.—SIGH— DO COME IN.

VITAMIN, THE PLAY WAS WONDERFUL—

AND SO WAS THAT TV PUBLICITY YOU GOT LAST WEEKEND—

PLEASE DON'T MENTION THAT!

VITAMIN, YOU SEEM AWFULLY DOWN—WHATEVER COULD BE WRONG?

AFTER ALL, YOUR NEW PLAY'S A HIT—THE MEDIA MADE YOU A HERO FOR NABBING THAT PICKPOCKET—

RICHARD, DIDN'T YOU HEAR THE SLANDEROUS PHRASE THAT TV PERSON BRANDED ME WITH?

THAT TV PERSON REFERRED TO ME AS "ALMOST IMMORTAL"!

DO YOU KNOW WHAT IT MEANS TO BE ALMOST IMMORTAL, RICHARD?

WHY IT'S PRECISELY THE SAME AS BEING MORTAL!

THE LASS ON THE NEWS CALLED ME "ALMOST" IMMORTAL—WHICH IS TO SAY, MORTAL! MY ATTORNEY SAYS I'VE NO GROUNDS FOR A SUIT.

VITAMIN, I'M AFRAID THERE'S NO WAY AROUND BEING MORTAL— IT'S JUST SOMETHING YOU'LL HAVE TO LIVE WITH.

I WONDER... I WONDER...

IMAGINE, VITAMIN SO DISTURBED BY THE MERE **SUGGESTION** HE MIGHT NOT LIVE **FOREVER!**

VITAMIN'S NEVER **FACED** HIS OWN MORTALITY— BUT THEN THAT'S SOMETHING FEW OF US EVER COME TO GRIPS WITH.

"I'M SURE HE'S HIS OLD SELF TODAY—"

AN 11 A.M. APPOINTMENT'LL BE FINE, DR. FREEZDREI. TILL TOMORROW, THEN...

DICK LOCHER MAX COLLINS

I SEE WHERE YOUR PAL FLINTHEART GOT SOME NICE PUBLICITY OUTA NAILIN' THAT DIP.*

* PICKPOCKET

VITAMIN TOOK OFFENSE WHEN THAT EYEWITNESS NEWS GAL CALLED HIM **"ALMOST** IMMORTAL—"

WHY? WAS HE PLANNIN' TO LIVE FOREVER?

"APPARENTLY," TRACY SAYS. EVEN NOW, VITAMIN SITS CONTEMPLATING HIS MORTALITY—

—AS HIS CHAUFFEURED LIMO WINDS ITS WAY UP A MOUNTAIN ROAD, ON IT'S WAY TO A SPECIFIC LOCATION:

...THE FREEZDREI INSTITUTE.

WELCOME, MR. FLINTHEART— THE DOCTOR IS EXPECTING YOU.

THANK YOU, M'DEAR.

GREETINGS, MR. FLINTHEART— I AM **DR. KRYOS FREEZDREI.**

I HARDLY EXPECTED TO BE MET AT THE DOOR BY THE FAMED DR. FREEZDREI HIMSELF.

THE FAMOUS MUST HONOR ONE ANOTHER, YES?

DICK LOCHER MAX COLLINS

"BESIDES, IT TAKES A MAN OF VISION TO EMBRACE **THE CRYONIC** PATH TO **IMMORTALITY**—"

ALLOW ME TO WARMLY WELCOME YOU TO THE FREEZDREI INSTITUTE.

"I BELIEVE I UNDERSTAND THE BASIC NOTION OF CRYONICS, DR. FREEZDREI," VITAMIN SAYS.

LET US SAY A PERSON SUCCUMBS TO A DISEASE—THE DECEASED IS THEN PROMPTLY **FROZEN**—

—CORRECT.

AT SOME FUTURE DATE, WHEN THE DISEASE CLAIMING ONE'S LIFE HAS BEEN CURED, ONE WOULD THEN BE **THAWED OUT**—

AND **REANIMATED**, AS IT WERE!

YOU'VE A GOOD BASIC UNDERSTANDING OF CRYONICS, MR. FLINTHEART.

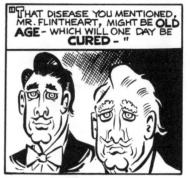

"THAT DISEASE YOU MENTIONED, MR. FLINTHEART, MIGHT BE **OLD AGE**—WHICH WILL ONE DAY BE **CURED**—"

A MIDDLE-AGED MAN LIKE M'SELF SEES "OLD AGE" ONLY IN THE FAR DISTANCE—

MR. FLINTHEART, IT NEVER HURTS TO PLAN AHEAD...

I REALIZE THOUGHTS OF OLD AGE ARE PREMATURE IN YOUR CASE, MR. FLINTHEART.

I'M IN MY PRIME, IN THE PINK, SIR!

BUT EVEN A...YOUNG MAN LIKE YOURSELF SHOULD MAKE CERTAIN **ARRANGEMENTS**.

"ALLOW ME TO TAKE YOU ON A LITTLE TOUR OF OUR FACILITY," DR. FREEZDREI SAYS.

HIBERNATORIUM

THIS IS THE HIBERNATORIUM—

WHY, IT'S **WARM** IN HERE—I EXPECTED A MAMMOTH **FREEZER**...

"THE 'SLEEPERS' ARE COOLED WITHIN THEIR INDIVIDUAL CAPSULES BY LIQUID NITROGEN," FREEZDREI EXPLAINS. "AT A TEMPERATURE OF −196° CENTIGRADE."

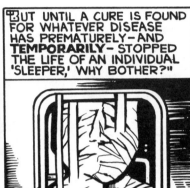

WHAT PRICE IMMORTALITY? $100,000.

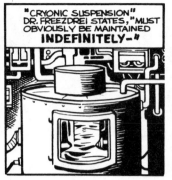

"CRYONIC SUSPENSION" DR. FREEZDREI STATES, "MUST OBVIOUSLY BE MAINTAINED INDEFINITELY—"

YOUR MONEY, INVESTED BY THE INSTITUTE IN A TRUST FUND, WILL PROVIDE CONSTANT CARE UNTIL YOUR EVENTUAL REANIMATION—

I REALIZE $100,000 IS A CONSIDERABLE SUM— WILL YOU TAKE A CHECK?

WHY, CERTAINLY— AS THE BARD SAID, "'TIS A TRIFLING FEE, FOR IMMORTAL-I-TEE-"

DID SHAKESPEARE SAY THAT? HE SHOULD HAVE! HAD THERE BEEN CRYONICS IN HIS DAY, HE MIGHT BE HERE SAYING IT NOW!

INVITING VITAMIN OVER FOR DINNER WAS A TERRIFIC IDEA, DICK— I THINK I CAN HEAR HIS CAR PULLING UP OUT FRONT...

HE'S BEEN SO DEPRESSED LATELY, I'M HOPING SOME COMPANY WILL CHEER HIM UP...

AH, RICHARD! ISN'T IT WONDERFUL TO BE ALIVE! AND WHERE'S YOUR LOVELY BRIDE?

SUMPTUOUS FEAST, TESS, M'DEAR! GLAD YOU ENJOYED IT, VITAMIN...

I DON'T WANT TO RAIN ON YOUR PARADE, VITAMIN— BUT ABOUT THIS CRYONICS BUSINESS...

YES? I THINK YOU SHOULD HEAR SOME FACTS OF LIFE—YOU'RE OLD ENOUGH...

SEVERAL "INSTITUTES"—NOT UNLIKE DR. FREEZDREI'S—HAVE PROVEN TO BE SCAMS...

RECENTLY ONE MAJOR "HIBERNATORIUM" WAS ABANDONED BY ITS FOUNDERS, LEAVING A GHASTLY, THAWING MESS BEHIND THEM...

BUT, RICHARD—THAT DOESN'T INVALIDATE CRYONICS ITSELF— NOR DR. FREEZDREI! VITAMIN, THERE'S MORE—

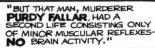

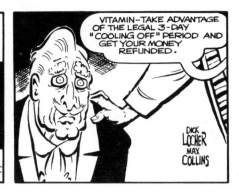

247

248

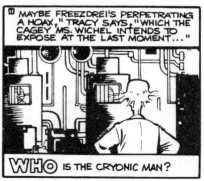

WILL 'CRYONIC MAN' WALK OUT OF DEEP FREEZE?

PRESS INTEREST IN DR. FREEZDREI'S **CRYONIC MAN** BUILDS...

DR. FREEZDREI CLAIMS HIS FULLY REANIMATED CRYONIC "SLEEPER" WILL REVOLUTIONIZE CONVENTIONAL NOTIONS OF DEATH...

AND, ADDING A NOTE OF MYSTERY, THE DOCTOR CLAIMS THE IDENTITY OF HIS 'CRYONIC MAN' WILL **SHOCK THE WORLD...**"

DISTINGUISHED MEMBERS OF THE PRESS—LADIES AND GENTLEMEN—WELCOME TO THE FREEZDREI INSTITUTE.

I HAVE INVITED YOU REPRESENTATIVES OF THE MEDIA TO THE FREEZDREI INSTITUTE— USHERED YOU INTO THE HIBERNATORIUM— TO WITNESS A HISTORIC EVENT—

TODAY THE TRIUMPH OF SCIENCE OVER DEATH ADVANCES FROM **THEORY** TO **FACT**—

TODAY YOU WILL SEE THE FIRST **CRYONIC MAN** WALK FROM THE CHILLY PAST INTO THE WARM PRESENT...

YOU NEED NOT SHIELD YOUR EYES, OR FEAR FOR THE COLD. THE ENTIRE PROCESS TAKES PLACE WITHIN THE CAPSULE—

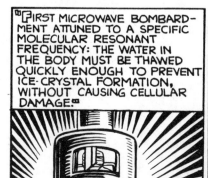

FIRST MICROWAVE BOMBARDMENT ATTUNED TO A SPECIFIC MOLECULAR RESONANT FREQUENCY: THE WATER IN THE BODY MUST BE THAWED QUICKLY ENOUGH TO PREVENT ICE-CRYSTAL FORMATION, WITHOUT CAUSING CELLULAR DAMAGE.

SECOND, THE BIOLOGIC 'ANTI-FREEZE' IN THE CRYONIC MAN'S BODY IS REPLACED WITH BLOOD—

HE'S ANSWERED EVERY QUESTION BUT ONE—

YEAH—WHO **IS** THE CRYONIC MAN?

THE PROCESS IS COMPLETE, LADIES AND GENTLEMEN—

OUR SLEEPER IS NOW MOST CERTAINLY ALIVE, IF NOT YET FULLY AWAKE...

DICK LOCHER MAX COLLINS

NONETHELESS, YOU ARE ABOUT TO MEET THE FIRST CRYONIC MAN...

MS. WICHEL'S NEWSPAPER HAS PROVIDED A PHYSICIAN TO ASCERTAIN WHETHER OR NOT THIS MAN IS INDEED ALIVE...

HAVE WE EVER MET, DOCTOR?

NO, WE HAVE NOT.

WHAT IS THIS, A MAGIC ACT?

MAYBE—AND IF THAT DOCTOR FINDS A HEARTBEAT IN THAT THAWED-OUT TV DINNER, IT'LL BE A GOOD TRICK...

DICK LOCHER MAX COLLINS

THIS MAN IS DEFINITELY ALIVE—HEARTBEAT QUITE REGULAR, IF SLOW...

DICK LOCHER MAX COLLINS

YOU SAID THE SLEEPER'S IDENTITY WOULD CONVINCE US THIS ISN'T A MAGIC ACT, FREEZDREI! QUIT STALLING—UNWRAP KING TUT!

TO THE EAGER GENTLEMAN WHO REQUESTED I "UNWRAP" KING TUT, I CAN ONLY SAY—MY PLEASURE.

DICK LOCHER MAX COLLINS

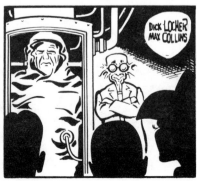

DICK LOCHER MAX COLLINS

IT CAN'T BE..

BUT IT IS·

"AND WHAT A HEADLINE IT'LL MAKE," WENDY SAYS. "THE CRYONIC MAN IS PRUNEFACE."

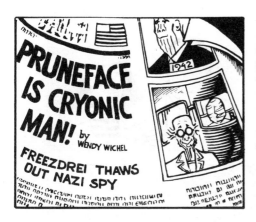

THE LAST I KNEW I WAS LEANING OUT A WINDOW IN A FREEZING STORM—

"—HOPING TO FIRE A SHOT AT **DICK TRACY**... AFRAID I'D **FREEZE** TO DEATH FIRST—"

NOW YOU TELL ME IT'S THIRTY-SOME YEARS LATER - **1983** ? YOU MUST BE JOKING...

DICK LOCHER MAX COLLINS

YOUR FEARS WERE VALID, PRUNEFACE - YOU **DID** FREEZE TO DEATH—

" BUT YOU WERE BROUGHT TO A HOSPITAL WHERE **I** WAS ON STAFF—"

I WAS ABLE TO QUICKLY- AND SECRETLY- TRANSFER YOU TO MY PRIVATE RESEARCH FACILITY, NEARBY—

DICK LOCHER MAX COLLINS

BUT IF I WAS **DEAD**...

THERE IS DEATH, AND THEN THERE IS **DEATH**—

" YOU WERE **CLINICALLY** DEAD - YOUR BREATHING AND HEARTBEAT HAD CEASED."

BY THE STANDARDS OF 30 YEARS AGO, YOU WERE EVEN **BIOLOGICALLY** DEAD...

DICK LOCHER MAX COLLINS

I WAS "BIOLOGICALLY" DEAD?

YES- MEANING RESUSCITATION BY THEN- CURRENT MEANS WAS IMPOSSIBLE.

DICK LOCHER MAX COLLINS

"BUT YOU WERE **NOT** IN A STATE OF **CELLULAR** DEATH—"

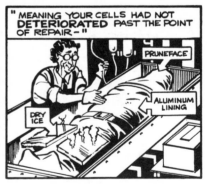

" MEANING YOUR CELLS HAD NOT **DETERIORATED** PAST THE POINT OF REPAIR—"

PRUNEFACE

ALUMINUM LINING

DRY ICE

JIM, WHAT'S THE JUSTICE DEPARTMENT OPINION? IF PRUNEFACE IS LEGALLY DEAD, THEN...?

NO CHARGES CAN BE BROUGHT AGAINST HIM? HARDLY- IF PRUNEFACE IS BREATHING, HE'LL BE CONSIDERED LEGALLY **ALIVE**—

DICK LOCHER MAX COLLINS

" AND THERE IS **NO** STATUTE OF LIMITATIONS ON **SEDITION**—"

YOU MUST BE DR. KRYOS FREEZDREI...

KRYOS FREEZDREI! I HAVE HEARD OF YOUR THEORIES ON FREEZING AND REANIMATION!

YES, AND THOUGH WE NEVER MET IN THE "GOOD OLD DAYS," I HAVE HEARD OF YOU—

DICK LOCHER
MAX COLLINS

AND OF YOUR HEROIC WORK FOR THE FATHER-LAND HERE AND ABROAD.

YOU FLATTER ME, SIR.

SHOULD THIS THAWED-OUT "CRYONIC MAN" PROVE SOMEHOW TO BE THE LEGITIMATE **PRUNEFACE**, THE LEGALITY IS CLEAR—

HE'S CONSIDERED LEGALLY **ALIVE**; HIS CRIMES—SEDITION, MURDER—ARE UNAFFECTED BY ANY STATUTE OF LIMITATIONS.

"RIGHT," INSPECTOR TRAILER SAYS. "BUT PRUNEFACE WAS NEVER BROUGHT TO TRIAL, REMEMBER—"

IN FACT, THE MANHUNT WAS SO QUICKLY LAUNCHED, NO OFFICIAL CHARGES HAD YET BEEN LEVELED AGAINST HIM!

DICK LOCHER
MAX COLLINS

WHAT ARE YOU SAYING, JIM?

WE MAY NOT HAVE A CASE—

"IF THIS IS INDEED PRUNEFACE," TRAILER SAYS, "HE MAY BE A **FREE** MAN—"

A MIRROR! BRING ME A MIRROR!

I'VE BEEN ASLEEP FOR OVER **30 YEARS**—I MUST SEE WHAT TOLL'S BEEN TAKEN!

WHY, IT'S A **MIRACLE**—I HAVEN'T AGED A DAY!

254

I HAVE HEARD OF YOUR RESEARCH, DR. FREEZDREI - BUT I HAD NO IDEA YOU'D COME SO FAR--

AT THE TIME OF YOUR "DEATH", I HAD NOT- BUT, THANKS TO THE UNFORTUNATE HAPPENSTANCE OF YOUR FREEZING -

A HUMAN GUINEA PIG, IF YOU WILL, HAD BEEN PROVIDED ME-"

DICK LOCHER MAX COLLINS

THE FBI SAYS THEY MAY NOT HAVE A CASE AGAINST PRUNEFACE?

IT'S BEEN OVER 30 YEARS-

TOO MANY WITNESSES ARE DEAD-TOO MUCH OF THE PHYSICAL EVIDENCE NO LONGER EXISTS...

DICK LOCHER MAX COLLINS

"THEN PRUNEFACE IS A FREE MAN" SAM SAYS.

I MUST GET UP! NO!

WHY MUST I STAY IN BED, DR. FREEZDREI? I'M NO CHILD!

HARDLY- YOU'RE WELL OVER 100 YEARS OLD.

BUT THERE ARE AFTEREFFECTS OF THE THAWING PROCESS - "FREEZER BURN", IF YOU WILL...

"BESIDES WHICH, BEFORE YOU 'FROZE TO DEATH', YOU INJURED YOUR LEG-AND IT STILL NEEDS TO HEAL"

DICK LOCHER MAX COLLINS

MY FIRST MEAL IN OVER 30 YEARS-

DICK LOCHER MAX COLLINS

A HOSPITAL MEAL, UNFORTUNATELY-ONE STEP AT A TIME, PRUNEFACE...

WEAK TEA JELLO BROTH

AND NOW I MUST RELAY SOME TRAGIC NEWS...

I DON'T KNOW HOW TO BREAK THIS TO YOU, BUT... WE LOST THE WAR.

NO... HOW COULD FATE BE SO UNKIND?

I'M AFRAID THERE'S MORE-

YOUR LOVELY, LOYAL BRIDE WAS FATE'S VICTIM AS WELL... OR RATHER, DICK TRACY'S...

DICK LOCHER MAX COLLINS

VITAMIN FLINTHEART, ALIVE AND WELL! AT YOUR SERVICE, SIR...

AND AS FAR AS THE WAR GOES, M'BOY—LET BYGONES BE BYGONES... IT WAS SO MANY YEARS AGO...

"YES — I FEEL THE **SAME WAY**," PRUNEFACE SAYS.

PRUNEFACE IS **LIVING PROOF** OF YOUR CRYONICS GENIUS, DOCTOR—

HIS REORIENTATION PROCESS IS JUST BEGINNING...

"**R**ETURNING FROM THE **PAST** INVOLVES READJUSTING TO THE **PRESENT**—"

SEEING A FAMILIAR FACE LIKE YOURS **IS** HELPFUL—

THOUGH POSSIBLY CONFUSING TO HIM—CONSIDERING HOW LITTLE I'VE AGED—

HOW'S THE LEG DOING?

BETTER. DOCTOR, CAN WE TALK? I HAVE A MILLION QUESTIONS...

WHAT'S GOING ON IN THE WORLD? WHO'S THE PRESIDENT?

RONALD REAGAN.

AN **ACTOR** FOR PRESIDENT? YOU'RE TRIFLING WITH ME—

NOT AT ALL— HERE'S HIS PICTURE...

WHY, THAT ISN'T RONALD REAGAN! THAT'S MY BROTHER LOUIE!

I'M AFRAID NOT— YOUR BROTHER PASSED AWAY MANY YEARS AGO...

THE WORLD **HAS** CHANGED.

ACCORDING TO THE HOSPITAL'S RECORDS, FREEZDREI WAS ON **STAFF** WHEN PRUNEFACE "DIED"!

"AND PRUNEFACE **WASN'T** *D.O.A.— JUST **NEARLY** FROZEN TO DEATH...

* DEAD ON ARRIVAL

BACK THEN WE'D HAVE USED AN ELECTRIC CHAIR TO THAW HIM OUT—

ONLY HE WAS PRONOUNCED DEAD HOURS LATER—AND LOOK WHO SIGNED THE DEATH CERTIFICATE..

DID YOU SEE THAT GUY?

WHAT A GREAT **MASK**! ASK HIM WHERE HE GOT IT!

EXCUSE ME, BUDDY— WHERE'D YOU ...

DICK LOCHER MAX COLLINS

UH, SORRY MISTER. ER— HAPPY HALLOWEEN ...

MISS, WOULD YOU HAPPEN TO HAVE THE TIME?

IT'S **MS.**, CREEP— AND KEEP YOUR DISTANCE!

MIZ? WHATEVER WAS **THAT** ABOUT? WHAT **IS** THIS WORLD I'VE WOKEN TO?

DICK LOCHER MAX COLLINS

I FEEL ADRIFT, HERE— A RELIC OF THE PAST WASHED UP ON A FUTURE SHORE ...

DICK LOCHER MAX COLLINS

TELEVISION SEEMED A MIRACLE, BACK THEN ... NOW PEOPLE WEAR 'EM ON THEIR WRISTS—

"'TECHNOLOGY,' AS THEY CALL IT, HAS COME FAR ... IS THERE NO PLACE FOR **PRUNEFACE** IN THIS MODERN WORLD?"

WELL, SOME OF THE OLD NEIGHBORHOOD LOOKS REASONABLY FAMILIAR—

DICK LOCHER MAX COLLINS

"PERHAPS THE MODERN SKYLINE I VIEWED, COMING IN, WAS DECEIVING—AND THIS IS STILL THE CITY I KNEW... "

AH— MY **FAVORITE** BAR ... BUT THERE SEEMS TO HAVE BEEN A CHANGE OF MANAGEMENT ...

HEEBIE JEEBIES

BAND TONITE The Nodes PUNK 'N' DISORDERLY

MY— WHAT AN INTERESTING HAIRDO. WHAT'S IT CALLED?

FRED.

BARKEEP— DRAW A DARK BEER, IF YOU WOULD. WASN'T THIS ESTABLISHMENT ONCE KNOWN AS "JOE'S"?

PROBABLY.

"MY WORD," PRUNEFACE SAYS, "WHAT'S GOING ON UP **THERE**?" "THAT'S ENTERTAINMENT—"

DICK LOCHER MAX COLLINS

SINCE I'M COMPLYING WITH ALL YOUR REQUESTS REGARDING MY PATIENT, I HAVE A REQUEST OF MY OWN...

CONDUCT ALL THE TESTS AT YOUR INSTITUTE? CERTAINLY, DOCTOR.

WHAT'S FREEZDREI TRYING TO **PULL?**

NOTHING. THAT'S WHAT WORRIES ME...

YOU'RE BEING MOST COOPERATIVE, DR. FREEZDREI.

ANYTHING TO AID THE FORCES OF **JUSTICE,** MR. TRACY.

"AND I THINK YOUR TESTING WILL ONLY SERVE TO PROVE MY SINCERITY."

THE MOBILE CRIME LAB HAS COMPARED THE FINGERPRINTS TAKEN HERE WITH PRUNEFACE'S PRINTS, CIRCA '43... **PERFECT MATCH.**

THE SUBJECT PASSED HIS POLYGRAPH WITH FLYING COLORS—

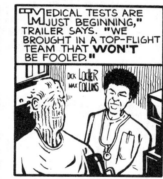

"MEDICAL TESTS ARE JUST BEGINNING," TRAILER SAYS. "WE BROUGHT IN A TOP-FLIGHT TEAM THAT **WON'T** BE FOOLED."

HOURS LATER—

AFTER EXTENSIVE EXAMINATION, I CAN ONLY CONCLUDE THAT DR. FREEZDREI DID INDEED CRYONICALLY REANIMATE THIS MAN—

I CONCUR.

I CONCUR.

GENTLEMEN, WE'VE COMPLIED WITH YOUR RIGOROUS TESTING FOR TWO DAYS, NOW— WHAT IS YOUR CONCLUSION?

OUR CONCLUSION IS THAT THIS MAN IS INDEED PRUNEFACE.

OUR REGRET IS THAT WE AREN'T ABLE TO PRESS ANY CHARGES AGAINST HIM— **AT THIS TIME—**

SURELY YOU AGREE WITH THE EXPERTS **NOW,** TRACY— PRUNEFACE **IS** PRUNEFACE.

YES HE IS— AND WE'VE DONE HIM AND DR. FREEZDREI A GREAT SERVICE—AT THE TAXPAYER'S EXPENSE...

"WE'VE VALIDATED FREEZDREI'S CRYONICS CLAIMS AND PAVED THE WAY FOR A **MULTI-MILLION DOLLAR** ENTERPRISE..."

265

WE'RE **PACKED,** PRUNEFACE — FOUR SUITCASES —

CONTAINING TWO TOOTH-BRUSHES AND 10 MILLION DOLLARS.

"A PRIVATE PLANE AWAITS US," FREEZDREI SAYS, "TO TAKE US TO OUR DESTINATION..."

SPLENDID, DOCTOR — BUT BEFORE WE TAKE LEAVE OF THESE FOUL UNITED STATES, THERE IS **ONE LAST MISSION** TO ACCOMPLISH —

IT'S ALMOST MIDNIGHT, SAM — GO ON HOME... I'LL WIND UP THESE REPORTS MYSELF...

"OKAY," SAYS SAM, "BUT BE CAREFUL DRIVING — THERE'S A **FREEZING RAIN** OUT THERE —"

THIS IS **MADNESS,** PRUNEFACE — WE COULD BE HALF-WAY TO LATIN AMERICA BY NOW!

ARE YOU QUESTION-ING A SUPERIOR, DOCTOR?

WHAT A **ROTTEN** NIGHT — THIS FREEZING RAIN MAKES DRIVING TREACHEROUS...

"WHAT'S THIS?" TRACY SAYS TO HIMSELF. "LOOKS LIKE THAT GUY'S GOT SOME TROUBLE... HECKUVA NIGHT TO GET STRANDED..."

CAN I BE OF HELP, MISTER? I'M A POLICE OFFICER...

WHAT'S THE TROUBLE? MAYBE I CAN GIVE YOU A LIFT TO A SERVICE STATION —

NO TROUBLE, MR. TRACY. BUT PERHAPS I CAN OFFER **YOU** A LIFT?

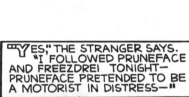

YOU MUST **NOT** DELAY, MR. CATCHEM— YOU HAVE ONLY AN HOUR TO SAVE YOUR FRIEND—

WHY ONLY AN HOUR? HELLO? **HELLO?**

"HE HUNG UP!" SAM SAYS.

I HOPE YOU'LL FORGIVE THIS **COOL** RECEPTION, MR. TRACY...

THE INSTRUMENT OF YOUR DESTRUCTION WILL BE **LIQUID NITROGEN**, MR. TRACY— BUT YOU'LL NOT **DROWN.**

THESE CAPSULES HAVE AN INNER SPACE BETWEEN TWO CHAMBERS— YOU'RE IN A CAPSULE WITHIN A CAPSULE—

"INTO THAT SPACE **FREEZING LIQUID** WILL SOON FLOW—"

DEAR— SHOULDN'T YOU CALL HQ?

NO!

WAITING FOR A WARRANT, PURSUING THIS OFFICIALLY, COULD MEAN A DELAY THAT COULD COST TRACY HIS **LIFE!**

"BUT, DEAR— AT LEAST TAKE TIME TO CALL IN LIZZ AND LEE—" "NO.— I'M GOING **ALONE!**"

THE LIQUID NITROGEN IS FLOWING, MR. TRACY— YOU'LL FREEZE TO DEATH **SLOWLY**, AS **I** FROZE!

WHY, HE'S PASSED OUT! HE WENT UNCONSCIOUS ALMOST **IMMEDIATELY!**

OF COURSE— DUE TO THE EXTREME COLD OF THE LIQUID NITROGEN.

I'M SORRY THAT TRACY NOT SUFFERING IS SUCH A BITTER DISAPPOINTMENT TO YOU, PRUNEFACE—

A MINOR DEFEAT, COMPARED TO **DICK TRACY'S.**

IT'S DONE.

THE GREAT DETECTIVE! **FROZEN STIFF!**

THIS IS **ONE** DEATH TRAP DICK TRACY DID **NOT** ESCAPE FROM!

MEANWHILE, SAM CATCHEM RACES TO RESCUE HIS PARTNER FROM A FATE THAT HAS ALREADY CLAIMED HIM...

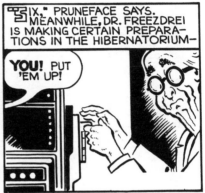

271

I GUESS THAT GUY ON THE PHONE WASN'T KIDDIN' WHEN HE SAID I ONLY HAD AN HOUR TO GET YOU OUTTA THAT JOINT...

WHILE...

I WONDER WHAT'S KEEPING DR. FREEZDREI?

IF YOU'RE WONDERING WHEN DR. FREEZDREI AND THE OTHERS WILL ARRIVE, I'M AFRAID THE ANSWER IS **NEVER**.

WHO... WHO ARE **YOU**?

THAT WILL BECOME CLEAR SOON ENOUGH.

WHAT..?

THERE'S BEEN A CHANGE OF FLIGHT PLANS, MISTER PRUNEFACE...

THERE'S BEEN A CHANGE OF DESTINATION. AND YOUR FRIENDS HAVE BEEN DETAINED — **PERMANENTLY**.

"WHAT IS THE MEANING OF THIS? WHO **ARE** YOU?"
"PLEASE HOLD OUT YOUR WRISTS."

BE REASONABLE—I'M A **RICH MAN**! SURELY WE CAN PUT THE PAST BEHIND US —

"THERE IS **NO** STATUTE OF LIMITATIONS ON **WAR CRIMES**, MR. PRUNEFACE—

"NOT WHERE SOME OF US ARE CONCERNED, AT LEAST...."

SO MUCH FOR FREEZDREI'S DREAM OF A CRYONIC FUTURE—

"FREEZDREI SEEMED TO BE IN THE PROCESS OF THAWING SOME OTHER SLEEPERS, BEFORE I INTERRUPTED HIM,"

"I WONDER WHO THEY WERE?" TRACY ASKS.

HE DOESN'T LOOK SO BAD, FOR A GUY WHO JUST **DIED**-

SAM, AS VITAMIN FLINTHEART MIGHT SAY.. I CAME, I THAWED, I CONQUERED.

OUCH! CAREFUL - A REMARK LIKE THAT COULD LAND YOU IN THE HOSPITAL ...

WHAT'S THE WORD ON PRUNEFACE AND FREEZDREI?

FREEZDREI DIED IN THE EXPLOSION AND FIRE AT THE INSTITUTE- POSITIVE I.D.

"AND HIS **CRYONIC DREAM** DIES WITH HIM," TRACY SAYS. "HE KEPT HIS DISCOVERIES TO HIMSELF, YOU KNOW."

NO WORD ON PRUNEFACE, THOUGH.

I THINK WE'VE SEEN THE LAST OF HIM.

DO YOU SUPPOSE THAT **STRANGER** WHO CALLED ME HAD SOMETHING TO DO WITH PRUNEFACE'S DISAPPEARANCE?

PERHAPS

"THE OLD TESTAMENT JUSTICE THAT CLAIMED FREEZDREI MAY ALSO HAVE CAUGHT UP WITH PRUNEFACE," TRACY SAYS.

"IN WHICH CASE, I DON'T THINK HE'LL BE COMING BACK, THIS TIME..."

FIVE OF FREEZDREI'S CRYONIC "SLEEPERS" WERE CAUGHT NAPPING IN THAT FIRE.

UNIDENTIFIABLE.

I GUESS THAT WRAPS THIS ONE UP... BUT I'D FEEL BETTER IF WE'D FOUND **PRUNEFACE** - OR HIS BODY.

SAM - SOME THINGS YOU JUST HAVE TO TAKE ON **FAITH** ...

DICK TRACY AT THE WAX MUSEUM

PRINCIPAL PERPETRATORS: **Harley Niav, AKA Putty Puss**

ORIGINALLY APPEARED: *June 4, 1989– September 24, 1989*

WRITER: *Max Allan Collins*   ARTIST: *Dick Locher*

Perhaps the greatest challenge for a writer and artist attempting to follow the lead of Chester Gould is coming up with suitably vile, appropriately grotesque villains.

Chet tended to develop his villains on the drawing board: Flattop, for instance, began as a sketch the artist made taking the commuter train from Chicago back home to rural Woodstock, Illinois. Other great foes, like Pruneface and B-B Eyes, began as doodles that grew into masterpieces of criminal characterization.

As a writer, my MO is necessarily different. I tend to begin with the subject matter—usually, the central crime I wish to explore—and attempt to develop an appropriate villain. Hence, a story of inner-city arson suggested Torcher—a dragon-like fiend whose red hair resembled a sea of flames. A recent story about dognapping featured bleary-eyed villain Bernard St. Claude, who resembled a Saint Bernard and whose darkened nose came from his constant tippling; and his wife, Teri—whose long blonde hair obscures her face in the manner of a Yorkshire terrier—who is actually top dog of their operation.

Rick Fletcher would usually request that I rough out a sketch of how I saw each villain, and further asked for any other supplementary material I might have. In the case of Torcher, my sketch was accompanied by photos of actors Dan Duryea and Robert Lansing, who seemed about the physical type I had in mind. Rick took this raw material and fashioned a terrific design for our arsonist.

Only on rare occasions have I sent villain sketches to Dick Locher; my written character descriptions seem to be enough to provide the spark. Often (as in the case of the aforementioned Bernard St. Claude and Teri) he comes up with something remarkably like my mental image; other times, as with the terrorist Hammerhead, he completely surprises me and surpasses what my mind's eye saw.

Our most popular villain to date, however, is (not surprisingly) a throwback to the Gould-style villain, where the crime itself is not as important as the fiend's appearance. The idea of a villain who can change his face to masquerade as others is not new. My specific inspiration for the character came from "Fearless Fosdick," Al Capp's spoof of "Tracy" that often appeared as a strip-within-the-strip in "Li'l Abner." Fosdick's archenemy Anyface had much in common with our Putty Puss.

But Putty Puss presented some new twists to this old idea. Actor Harley Niav is able to mold his face into a replica of another's; but after an hour his face begins to lose shape and shift, as if melting, until his masquerade is over and he is again exposed as the blobby-faced madman, Putty Puss. (Of late, readers have frequently pointed out that the 1990 film *Darkman*—which the first Putty Puss continuity predates considerably—uses both the concept of synthetic flesh *and* a time limit for that flesh, before "melting.")

Dick Locher and I knew enough *not* to bump Putty Puss off; we knew we had hold of a good one. Chester Gould would have shown no such mercy. But from our point of view, a good fiend is hard to find.

Fans demanded a second Putty Puss story, and we gave it to them, barely a year after the first one. And do you know what? We may not have seen the last of him, either . . . .

BED REST IS A **MUST**, MR. PLENTY—

BOSH!

"THE DOCTOR HAS TOLD B.O.— WHO FEARED HE'D CAUGHT A "COMPUTER VIRUS"— TO GET SOME REST—

I CAIN'T MISS OPENIN' DAY AT THE AMUSIN' PORK!

NOW, B.O.—

"WE HAVE **PLENTY** OF HELP AT THE AMUSEMENT PARK, DEAR—"

LAND O' PLENTY AMUSEMENT PARK

YE DON'T HAVE "PLENTY" LESSEN YE GOT B.O. PLENTY!

"ASIDES, GERTRUDE, I'M AFEERED TO LEAVE YE ALONE WITH THAT MACRAME ATOLL, VITAMIN FLINTHORN!"

DICK LOCHER
MAX COLLINS

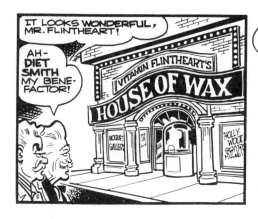

IT LOOKS **WONDERFUL**, MR. FLINTHEART!

AH— **DIET SMITH** MY BENE-FACTOR!

VITAMIN FLINTHEART'S
HOUSE OF WAX
ROGUE GALLERY   HOLLY-WOOD STAR

YOU HAVE ALLOWED ME TO REALIZE A LONG-CHERISHED **DREAM**— MY OWN **WAX MUSEUM**—

"WELL", SAYS DIET, "THE LAND O' PLENTY IS THE PERFECT PLACE FOR IT."

YOU'RE DOING MUCH, MUCH BETTER—

THANK YOU, DOCTOR— BUT WHAT ABOUT MY **PAROLE**?

AH **CAIN'T** BE BED-RIDDLED! OPENIN' DAY OF THE AMUSIN PARK IS COMIN' UP!

IF YOU TAKE **CARE** OF YOURSELF, B.O., MAY-BE YOU'LL BE UP AND AROUND BY THEN.

DICK LOCHER
MAX COLLINS

"BUT I GOT **CHORES** TO DO AFORE THEN, GERTRUDE"

VERY IMPRESSIVE, VITAMIN.

VITAMIN FLINTHEART'S
HOUSE OF WAX
ROGUE GALLERY   HOLLY-WOOD STAR

I'D FORGOTTEN YOU PERFORMED IN **HORROR** FILMS, VITAMIN—

THOSE WERE **LEAN** YEARS—

BUT "THE MUMMY'S BROTHER-IN-LAW" AND "DRACULA MEETS THE BOWERY BOYS" **DID** PAY THE RENT, MY DEAR FELLOW—

DIET SMITH, PROPRIETOR OF THE LAND O' PLENTY AMUSEMENT PARK, GETS AN ADVANCE LOOK AT IT'S LATEST ATTRACTION—

VITAMIN, YOUR **WAX** MUSEUM IS WONDERFUL!

AND FRIGHTENING!

ALMOST AS FRIGHTENING AS THE MEMORY OF HAVING TO STOOP TO PERFORMING IN GRADE-**Z** HORROR FILMS!

BUT THERE ARE **FEARS** YET TO BEHOLD THAT FAR **OUT DISTANCE** ANY CREATURE OF THE CINEMA—

YE GODS, VITAMIN— YOU'RE **RIGHT!** THESE MONSTERS DISTURB ME **MUCH** MORE!

BUT THEN, I **KNEW** SOME OF THEM!

REALITY **DOES** OUT DISTANCE FANTASY—

WHAT HOLLYWOOD CREATION COULD APPROACH THE HUMAN **HORROR** OF **THIS** CREATURE?

"PUTTY PUSS!" SAYS DIET.

DOCTOR, I CAN'T TELL YOU HOW MUCH THESE SESSIONS MEAN TO ME—

YOU'VE COME TO GRIPS WITH THE PAST TRAUMAS THAT "CREATED" PUTTY PUSS-
"I STILL HAVE NIGHTMARES ABOUT THE 'ACCIDENT,'" ADMITS HARLEY NIAV (A.K.A. PUTTY PUSS).

IT'S UNDERSTANDABLE- EVEN INEVITABLE- THAT YOU WOULD CONTINUE TO HARBOR BITTERNESS, AND EVEN RAGE-
YES-
"I WAS A HANDSOME, BRILLIANT ACTOR, AT THE HEIGHT OF MY CAREER!"
AND THEN A JEALOUS FELLOW ACTOR SABOTAGED MY CAR-RESULTING IN A HIDEOUSLY DISFIGURING "ACCIDENT"-
DICK LOCHER
MAX COLLINS

IT'S POSSIBLE THAT THE TRAUMA OF YOUR DISFIGURING "ACCIDENT" ALONE MIGHT'VE BEEN SOMETHING YOU COULD DEAL WITH-
I AGREE-
"BUT THEN," PUTTY PUSS CONTINUES, "PLASTIC SURGEON WILL CARVER ENTERED, STAGE LEFT-"
PROMISING TO RESTORE MY PHYSICAL BEAUTY WITH A NEW TECHNIQUE-
DICK LOCHER
MAX COLLINS

HARLEY NAIV, a.k.a. PUTTY PUSS, IS IN SESSION WITH HIS PSYCHIATRIST AT THE STATE HOSPITAL FOR THE CRIMINALLY INSANE -
HARLEY, THE TRAUMA OF YOUR FAILED PLASTIC SURGERY WOULD DRIVE ANY SANE MAN OVER THE BRINK-
IT DROVE ME TO CRIME-
A HANDSOME, BRILLIANT ACTOR, DISFIGURED BY A JEALOUS COLLEAGUE ...

"... PROMISED A RETURN TO PHYSICAL PERFECTION BY A QUACK PLASTIC SURGEON, WHOSE 'SYNTHETIC FLESH' LEFT ME A **FREAK**."

"BUT A **GIFTED** FREAK: I LEARNED, WHILE INSTITUTIONALIZED, HOW TO **RESHAPE** MY PUTTY-LIKE PHYSIOGOMY INTO ITS FORMER STATE!"

"THIS RESTORATION WAS **BRIEF** - BUT **WONDROUS!**"

AND THEN I TAUGHT MYSELF TO SHAPE MY MALLEABLE FACE INTO THE FACE OF **OTHERS** -

"AND THE CRIMINAL MASTERMIND, THE **MAN OF A MILLION FACES**, WAS BORN!"

DICK LOCHER
MAX COLLINS

BUT NOW I'M **CURED** - AND READY TO BE **PAROLED** -

WELL...

TELL ME, DOCTOR- WOULD YOU SAY I'M **NORMAL** AGAIN?

DICK LOCHER
MAX COLLINS

"AM I READY TO PASS A **SANITY** HEARING?"

AM I FINALLY READY TO REGAIN MY **FREEDOM?**

WELL...

I'M AFRAID, CONSIDERING THE SERIOUSNESS NOT ONLY OF YOUR **CONDITION**...

"... BUT OF THE **CRIMES** YOU COMMITTED ..."

DICK LOCHER
MAX COLLINS

...YOUR RELEASE IS **NOT** IMMINENT.

EVEN THOUGH I'M **SANE** AGAIN?

283

TRACY INVESTIGATES THE ESCAPE OF HARLEY NAIV, a.k.a. PUTTY PUSS.

THE DEATH OF DR. MITCIV IS A TRAGIC LOSS—

WHEN PUTTY PUSS WAS ADMITTED TO YOUR FACILITY, WARDEN, I WARNED YOU OF HIS UNIQUE "TALENT."

I KNOW, DETECTIVE TRACY— BUT OUR SECURITY IS TIGHT, AND HARLEY NIAV WAS KEPT UNDER STRICT SUPERVISION—

"BUT WE ARE A HOSPITAL, AND WE TRY TO HELP OUR PATIENTS RETURN TO SANITY."

DR. MITCIV'S SESSIONS WITH HARLEY NIAV WERE NECESSARILY PRIVATE—

GIVING PUTTY PUSS A STAGE FOR MURDER AND MASQUERADE!

LOOK AT THIS, TRACY— PUTTY PUSS HAS MADE AWAY WITH A BUNDLE OF DRUGS— SEDATIVES, MOSTLY.

FOR STREET SALE?

I DON'T THINK SO—

"I THINK OUR ESCAPEE MAY RECOGNIZE THAT HE'S SICK," SAYS TRACY, "AND IS HOPING TO TREAT HIMSELF."

VARIETY

HE PORTRAYED A DOCTOR IN A TV MINI-SERIES, AND GAINED CONSIDERABLE MEDICAL KNOWLEDGE—

ACTOR HARLEY NIAV DID GET CARRIED AWAY WITH HIS ROLES—

YES—GAINING AND LOSING WEIGHT WHEN A PART CALLED FOR IT—

"RESEARCHING THE FILM ROLE OF A CRIMINAL, NIAV ESTABLISHED UNDERWORLD CONTACTS THAT MADE HIS LATER ROLE—

—A SNAP!"

286

RICHARD!!

YOUR WAX MUSEUM LOOKS **IMPRESSIVE,** VITAMIN—

THANK YOU, RICHARD— MY ABJECT APOLOGIES FOR SUMMONING YOU SO **ABRUPTLY!**

HELPING A FRIEND IS **NO TROUBLE,** VITAMIN— NOW WHAT'S THIS ABOUT A **BLACKMAILER?**

I APPEARED ON STAGE WITH **HARLEY NIAV** ON NUMEROUS OCCASIONS—A **BRILLIANT** ACTOR!

HAS **PUTTY PUSS** BEEN IN CONTACT WITH YOU?

YES. YOU SEE, WHEN I WAS **YOUNGER** ...THIS IS DIFFICULT.

I'M AFRAID, RICHARD, THAT YOU WILL LOSE **RESPECT** FOR ME, UPON LEARNING MY **SECRET**—

VITAMIN, I'M NOT CONCERNED ABOUT SOME PAST INDISCRETION OF YOURS. YOU'RE A **GOOD** MAN, AND A GOOD **FRIEND**—

IF HARLEY NIAV HAS COME OUT OF THE PAST TO **BLACK-MAIL** YOU, MY **ONLY** CONCERN IS TO **NAIL** THAT MADMAN!

I **KNEW** I COULD DEPEND ON YOU, RICHARD—COME... I'LL GIVE YOU THE **DETAILS.**

BUT **FIRST**—ALLOW ME TO GIVE YOU A BRIEF ADVANCE TOUR—

DICK TRACY'S ROGUES' GALLERY

"YOU'VE SOME **OLD FRIENDS** TO GREET..."

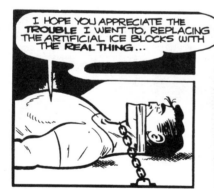

294

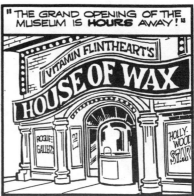

296

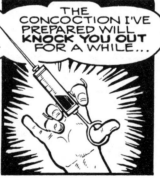

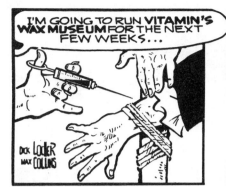

"THE WAX MUSEUM WILL OPEN IN A FEW **HOURS**." AND WHEN THOSE HOURS HAVE QUICKLY PASSED -

I WISH DADDY COULD BE WITH US.

SO DO I, JOE.

GERTRUDE, YE BEST STAY AWAY FROM THET CONSARNED LETHARGIO, VITALSIGNS FLINTHEAD!

HIS DETENTIONS AIN'T HORRIBLE!

HUSH, B.O. - MR. FLINTHEART IS A PERFECT GENTLEMAN. UNLIKE **CERTAIN** PEOPLE.

I'M WORRIED ABOUT TRACY -

WE SHOULDN'T EVEN **MENTION** THAT, SAM - HE'S ON A TOP-SECRET ASSIGNMENT!

"DON'T BE A **DUMMY**, SAM!" SAYS LIZZ.

PAT, I'M **WORRIED** ABOUT DICK - THIS SUDDEN "TOP SECRET" GOVERNMENT ASSIGNMENT DOESN'T RING **TRUE** -

TESS, I AGREE WITH YOU- TRACY'S LAST SECOND "TOP-SECRET" MISSION STRIKES ME AS SUSPICIOUS, TOO -

"AND I INTEND CHECKING INTO IT - AS FAST AS I CAN."

YE GODS... PUTTY PUSS WAS **RIGHT** - I AM PARALYZED - AND ON DISPLAY!

"PUTTY PUSS IS AT LARGE, SAM! HE'S IMITATED TRACY BEFORE!"

TOO BAD VITAMIN COULDN'T ATTEND HIS OWN OPENING.

JEEZ, I NEVER THOUGHT OF THAT! BUT THE VOICE WAS PERFECT!

HARLEY NIAV WAS — AND IS — A GREAT ACTOR! A MASTER MIMIC!

"HEY, YOU COULD BE RIGHT! WHAT SHOULD WE DO?"

KEEP YOUR EYES OPEN — THIS WAX MUSEUM WAS WHERE TRACY WAS LAST HEADED!

BUT WHERE COULD HE BE?

IT'S A LONG SHOT THAT TRACY WOULD STILL BE HERE, BUT IT'S A PLACE TO START —

WE CAN HAVE A LOOK AROUND...

... AND CHECK WITH VITAMIN — HE'LL BE ABLE TO HELP!

NO... NO...

TOO BAD WE CAN'T ASK DICK HERE FOR A HAND —

DICK LOCHER
MAX COLLINS

THAT WAX FIGURE DOES LOOK LIFELIKE —

YOU ALMOST EXPECT TRACY TO TALK —

DICK LOCHER
MAX COLLINS

IF I ONLY COULD...

LIZZ! SAMUEL! WHAT DO YOU THINK OF MY EXHIBIT?

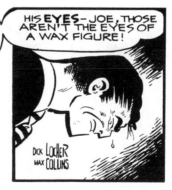

304

305

307